W9-BVD-006

contemporary topics in
EXPERIMENTAL PSYCHOLOGY

GENERAL EDITORS: JAMES DEESE

LEO J. POSTMAN

THE PERCEPTION OF BRIGHTNESS AND DARKNESS

LEO M. HURVICH

and

DOROTHEA JAMESON

Department of Psychology
University of Pennsylvania

ALLYN AND BACON, INC.

BOSTON   *1966*

To the Young J's & H's

© Copyright 1966 by Allyn and Bacon, Inc., 150 Tremont Street, Boston. All rights reserved. No part of this book may be reproduced in any form, by mimeograph or any other means, without permission in writing from the publisher.

Library of Congress Catalog Card Number: 66–15487

Printed in the United States of America

Foreword

THE EXPLOSIVE GROWTH OF KNOWLEDGE in psychology makes it increasingly difficult to treat in depth all important topics in a single course. One solution for this difficulty might be called the *survey in depth*. The instructor takes it as his responsibility to cover some comprehensive body of material, but he does so, when practicable, *by example*. The object is to allow the student to work with difficult problems that are representative of a larger body of problems. The survey in depth can accomplish this because any one problem will illustrate the methods, ways of thinking, techniques, and kinds of results characteristic of a wide range of problems. Thus, the study of the perception of brightness can illustrate, by example, a great many of the aspects of the study of perception as a whole.

The present series is designed to present the student such a survey in depth of the various fields of experimental psychology. The intent of the series is not to provide a comprehensive survey of the textbook variety but to present, as examples, some representative problems within each of the major areas of psychology that are, in whole or in part, experimental in nature. The series is addressed to the undergraduate student in psychology. Each volume could also serve, however, as a basic text in some specialized area, or as supplementary material in a large-scale introductory course.

Experimental psychology is both a series of substantive fields and a collection of methods. In this series, some balance is kept between both aspects of experimental psychology. Each volume deals with particular methodological issues. The student is not presented with a series of *faits accomplis*, but he is introduced to ways in which problems can be solved by appeal to experimental data.

Each book in the series is a self-sufficient unit that does not depend on supplementary instruction or expert guidance. It is this feature which, we hope, will make the books in this series of very broad general interest.

James Deese

Leo J. Postman

Preface

switch on the light
so it gets dark outside
and we can go
to bed.

ANSELM HOLLO

IN THIS BOOK we bring together discussions of a variety of phenomena and experiments that are rarely given more than a cursory review in psychological textbooks. We believe, furthermore, that the diverse phenomena are best treated in a single context rather than subdivided, for example, into sensory versus perceptual categories. An understanding of sensory threshold phenomena and of the different parameters of the stimulus and physiological state that affect the threshold is basically relevant, for example, to the understanding of brightness constancy and contrast perceptions. Each separate problem area that is examined points up general properties of the visual response system, and the concept that we have found most helpful in approaching a broad understanding of visual behavior is the bimodal nature of the physiological response mechanism. It is only from the interplay of opposite response systems, brightening responses and darkening responses, that both the variety and the stability of our light perceptions emerge. If this book gives the student a sense of familiarity with the experimental procedures, the logic of interpretations of experimental findings, and some insight into the organized complexity of our perception of brightness and darkness, it will have satisfied our primary aim.

The limited number of references cited at the end of each chapter will provide guidelines for further reading for the interested student. The visual literature is an enormous one, and we are, of course, indebted to the authors of hundreds of articles that remain uncited here.

We wish to thank the publishers of *The Nation* for permission to use the stanza from the poem "Age Four" by Anselm Hollo and John Wiley & Sons for permission to reprint a portion of a table from *Color: A Guide to Basic Facts and Concepts*. Mr. Dean Yager made several helpful suggestions for changes in the original manuscript, and we are grateful for the patience and competence with which our secretary, Mrs. Evelyn Hankinson, handled the typing.

Research basic to the analyses and interpretations presented here was supported by grants from the National Science Foundation and from the National Institutes of Health. Preparation of the manuscript was also aided by a Fellowship award to Leo M. Hurvich from the John Simon Guggenheim Foundation.

Leo M. Hurvich

Dorothea Jameson

Philadelphia, Pennsylvania

Contents

I

Perceptual Ordering of
Apparent Brightness

As WE LOOK AROUND US, it is obvious that our visual world is made up of an array of objects, surfaces, and spaces that have different apparent brightnesses. If we are among the large majority of the population that has fully developed color vision, then the world that we see is also differentiated in terms of different color qualities—reds, greens, blues, and yellows. In this book, however, we shall not be concerned at all with the perception of different colored hues, but we shall abstract from the total complex of our visual perceptions those aspects concerned with brightness perception. In a different way we do this with a camera when we take a black and white photograph or when we view a conventional black and white television screen. How are we to develop meaningful specifications for the different brightness impressions that we have and for the stimuli that give rise to them?

It hardly needs saying that the same light stimulus produces a different brightness impression depending on the circumstances under which it is seen. The very same source may appear dazzlingly bright at night and yet be barely noticeable during daylight hours. What we want first is to assign some sort of meaningful designation which will specify the light as a visual stimulus, and it is clear that for this purpose the subjective brightness impression that a light makes cannot be used.

RADIANT ENERGY

In what way, then, can we meaningfully specify the light output properties of a stimulus source? The first thought that comes to mind for the ordinary lamps we are most familiar with is to state what the "watts" are. "Replace it with a 100-watt bulb," we say, or "It's too bright, try a 25-watt bulb." This is a sensible step. Light is a very small part of the electromagnetic spectrum of radiant energy. In addition to those rays that can be seen, namely, light rays, there are gamma rays, X-rays, ultraviolet rays, infrared rays, and radio and television rays. Since all radiant energy can be evaluated in power terms, that is, work per unit of time, it is reasonable to evaluate light or any other portion of the electromagnetic spectrum in watts. Watts simply expresses power in ergs per second ($1 \text{ w} = 1.003 \times 10^7$ ergs/sec), and *radiant flux*, which is a sample of radiant energy that is being transferred from a source to an intercepting surface, is measured in watts.

Although every real light source has a finite size, it is convenient to regard it as made up of a large number of points, and each point has some specifiable *radiant intensity* which determines the radiant energy it can emit per unit of time. If we consider one such point to be placed at the center of a sphere and to emit radiant flux uniformly in all directions, we can isolate a unit solid angle (one steradian) and specify the number of watts in this unit solid angle. For real sources of finite size we speak of the *radiant emittance* or *radiance*, which takes the totality of points into consideration. Thus, we have watts per steradian per square meter of the source area.

One more item completes our specification of energy in so-called radiometric terms. This is the concept of *irradiance* which gives us the density of the radiant flux that arrives at a surface, the density of the radiant flux that irradiates the surface.

PHOTOMETRIC CONCEPTS

The radiometric concepts are fundamental in the physical specifications of sources, but they are, of course, equally applicable to any wavelength region of the electromagnetic spectrum, for example, to gamma radiation or to those wavelengths used in television broadcasting. For the region of the electromagnetic spectrum that is perceived as *light* by a human observer, certain conventions have been adopted in order to specify radiant sources in relation to their light evocative capacities, and these conventions convert the radiometric concepts to photometric ones. (How the light evocative capacity of radiant energy is actually determined is discussed in Chapter II.) Most light specifications derive from the needs of industry, commerce, and the consumer, and for these specifications photometric measures are much more common than radiometric measures. Although the visual scientist often needs to have measures of the absolute or relative radiant energy of the light sources that he uses in his study of the physiological mechanisms of vision, he also finds the photometric specifications both useful and convenient to label his stimuli.

In photometric terms, radiant flux that is visually effective becomes *luminous flux*. Only in the wavelength region between, roughly, 380 nm and 800 nm is radiant flux visually effective. Suppose we had three sources of radiation, one of which emits X-rays, and the other two radiation at 400 nm and 550 nm, respectively. Suppose further that each source has the same radiant flux. Is the luminous flux also the same? The answer is "no." The first source has no luminous flux at all, the 400 nm source some small amount of luminous flux, and the 550 nm source a much larger amount. This is so because the sensitivity of the eye to different wavelengths of light varies markedly. The relation between *radiant* flux and *luminous* flux is a different one for different wavelengths of light and thus for different light sources. To determine the relation requires that we know the responses to the physical energies that are made by the human observer viewing these energies, as we shall see in Chapter II. For the moment we need only remember that the photometric measures ultimately depend on the visual responses to radiant energy by a human observer.

The unit of *luminous intensity* is called, appropriately enough, a *candle*, and was originally based on a standard wax candle. If a uniform point source of 1 candle in luminous intensity is placed at the center of a sphere, the luminous flux in a unit solid angle of that sphere is, by definition, 1 *lumen*. Since the solid angle of the entire sphere is 4π, the total flux emitted by such a light source is 4π lumens or 12.57 lumens.

Luminance is the photometric counterpart of radiance which, we remember, is the radiant flux emitted per unit solid angle per unit of surface for a source of finite size. Luminance is the most commonly used photometric unit and refers to the luminous flux radiated from a spatially extended source. It is the luminous flux per steradian (lumens) that leaves a unit area of the surface in the direction of measurement. Luminance applies not only to primary, self-luminous sources but also to secondary sources like a surface that reflects light. Representative values are given in Table 1.

The luminance concept is easily visualized in relation to candle-power. If we take a point source whose luminous intensity is 1 candle and think of it as expanded to an area of 1 cm², then this area would

Table 1*

Representative luminance values for different conditions of illumination

Illumination condition	Millilamberts
Direct sunlight	8250
Daylight out-of-doors	0.3×10^3 to 0.3×10^4
Good interior lighting	30 to 300
Moderate interior lighting	3 to 30
Feeble interior lighting	0.3 to 3
Outdoor lighting by night in a city	0.03 to 0.3
Night vision	0.3×10^{-4} to 0.03

* After LeGrand, but based on other photometric units.

have a luminance of 1 candle/cm². Candles per square centimeter is, in fact, a basic measure of luminance, although most researchers in the United States tend to prefer the _millilambert_ (ml) which is a specification of the _lumens_ emitted _per unit area_ of the emitting source rather than of the number of candles per unit area.

When we begin to list alternative units, it becomes obvious that the luminance specifications of light stimuli can lead to some confusion. Reading the scientific literature has its annoyances, in fact, because it sometimes seems that no two researchers use the same units. But the confusion is more apparent than real. In the last analysis, the luminance unit used depends simply on whether one is using, on the one hand, the candle or the lumen, and on the other, the English or metric system, to express the unit ratio. There are many tables available which give the simple multiplicative factors necessary to transform another man's preferences into one's own. Table 2 summarizes some of the more common units and their relations to one another.

The measure of light falling on a surface is _illuminance_, and this photometric term is comparable to irradiance in energy terms. The illumination or illuminance on a surface on which 1 lumen falls per square foot is the foot candle—or meter candle if the lumen is incident on a square meter. It is important to note that the illuminance on a surface does not depend on the nature of the surface itself. If a piece of white paper and a piece of black cloth receive the same amount of luminous flux per unit area, they are equally illuminated. Their luminances are, of course, not the same. Why? (See Chapter VI.)

One additional point: If we view a surface of some fixed luminance, we can easily check the fact that, with all other conditions remaining constant, we can decrease the brightness of the field by introducing in

Table 2

Relations among common photometric units

	Candle/cm² (Stilb)	Lambert (Lumens/cm²)	Candle/in.²	Millilambert	Candle/m² (Nit)	Lumen/m²
Candle/cm² (Stilb)	1 —	3.183×10^{-1} $1/\pi$	1.550×10^{-1} $1/A$	3.183×10^{-4} $1/\pi \times 10^{-3}$	10^{-4} $1/F$	3.183×10^{-5} $1/\pi F$
Lambert (Lumens/cm²)	3.1416 π	1 —	4.869×10^{-1} π/A	10^{-3} —	3.1416×10^{-4} π/F	10^{-4} $1/F$
Candle/in.²	6.452 A	2.054 A/π	1 —	2.054×10^{-3} $A/\pi \times 10^{-3}$	6.452×10^{-4} $1/E$	2.054×10^{-4} $1/E\pi$
Millilambert	3.1416×10^{3} $\pi \times 10^{3}$	10^{3} —	4.869×10^{2} $\pi/A \times 10^{3}$	1 —	3.1416×10^{-1} $\pi/F \times 10^{-3}$	10^{-1} $1/F \times 10^{3}$
Candle/m² (Nit)	10^{4} F	3.183×10^{3} F/π	1.550×10^{3} E	3.183 $F/\pi \times 10^{-3}$	1 k	3.183×10^{-1} $1/\pi$
Lumen/m²	3.1416×10^{4} πF	10^{4} F	4.869×10^{3} πE	10 $F \times 10^{-3}$	3.1416 π	1 —

Notation for Symbols: $\pi = 3.1416$, $A = 6.452 = (cm/in.)^2$, $E = 1550 = (in./m)^2$, $F = 10^4 = (cm/m)^2$.

To convert from one unit to another, read up or down from the diagonal. For example, 1 millilambert = .002054 candles/in.². (After Burnham, Hanes, & Bartelson.) Data compiled by K. S. Weaver.

front of the eye an aperture smaller than the size of the natural pupil. Constriction of the natural pupil produces the same effect. Because of changes in pupil size, *retinal illuminance* is not the same as the illuminance of the cornea of the eye. To take account of the fact that retinal illuminance is not equal to the external luminance, a unit called the *troland* has been introduced. It is defined as the retinal illuminance produced by an external luminance of 1 candle/m² viewed through an entrance pupil 1 mm² in area. With a knowledge of pupil size for different external luminances the conversion from *millilamberts* to *trolands* can readily be made. However, there is some question now of the usefulness of this "correction" to trolands. The research of Stiles and Crawford indicates that light that enters the eye eccentrically through the pupil has less physiological effectiveness than light rays entering near the center of the pupil. In any event, to eliminate possible effects of varying pupil size, either a delimiting artificial pupil may be used, or if the experiment involves optical apparatus, the size of the image produced by the lenses may be kept smaller than the size of the natural pupil.

With a system of conventional photometric units, we can obviously order the various self-luminous or illuminated objects in our field of view in terms of their various luminances. There are numerous light-sensing devices that are commercially available for photometric measurements, and with such a device we can specify precisely, in luminance units, how different one light stimulus is from another.

PSYCHOPHYSICAL SCALING FUNCTIONS

Is this luminance ordering and are these photometric differences the same as the brightness ordering and brightness differences of a perceptual scale that we might develop for the appearances associated with the different specified light stimuli? The answer is clearly "no" if we permit the viewing conditions to vary, for our discussion started with the fact that one and the same light can appear very dim or glaringly bright under different circumstances. But suppose we restrict ourselves to a single condition of observation, and, let us say, we expose only one illuminated stimulus field at a time in an otherwise darkened room, fix both the size of the stimulus and the duration of its exposure at constant values, and look directly at it so that the stimulus always falls on the same, central part of our retina, the fovea. Will the apparent brightnesses of a series of separately exposed stimuli even then be directly proportional to their luminance specifications? To answer this question, we must be able to compare directly a scale of measured photometric luminance values with a scale of measured perceived brightnesses for the same stimuli. And as soon as we raise this question, we must come to grips with a problem that is at the heart of that area of psychology that is known as psychophysics and one that is crucial to much psychological measurement. Now we are asking specifically what the relation is between a dimension of measureable stimulus units, on the one hand, and a dimension of psychologically observable, perceptual units, on the other. How are we to measure units along the psychological dimension?

Discriminability Scales; Fechner's Law

Let us consider some of the experimental procedures that might be used to set up a psychological scale of perceived apparent brightness. One of the classical psychophysical methods for perceptual scaling is based on discriminability between two stimuli. Suppose we start our experiment in a dark room with a central, foveally fixated test field in which we can expose lights of continuously variable luminance. Assume that the test field is at first dark, and our test light is then turned up until it appears to be just-perceptibly brighter than the totally dark test area with which we started. We measure the luminance of this light with our photometer, and we record this luminance value as the first step on our brightness scale. Starting from this minimally bright test field, we may now increase the luminance again until the observer reports that the test area has become just-perceptibly brighter than it was. This second luminance value, which appears just-perceptibly brighter than the first one, now represents the point on the stimulus scale that is equivalent to the second step on our perceptual scale. The experiment may be continued progressively with each consecutive step representing a just-perceptible increase in apparent brightness over the previous one until we have reached the maximal brightness level that can be obtained. In practice, there are many variables that enter into such measures of brightness discrimination, but we shall postpone a more detailed analysis of the discrimination problem itself until a later chapter.

Our concern at present is to make some general observations about the approximate results of such a scaling procedure. Had we carried out a discrimination scaling experiment of the sort we just described, then we would have as our measures, a photometric luminance value for each stimulus, on the one hand, and the number of the associated just-noticeable-brightness step, on the other. We have already said that to translate one system of photometric units into another, say, millilamberts to candles per square meter, we need only multiply all of the units expressed in one system by an appropriate factor to convert them to the other system. The different photometric units are proportional to one another. There is, however, no a priori reason to anticipate simple proportionality between photometric stimulus units and psychological units of apparent brightness. And, indeed, if we were to plot the data of our just-noticeable-difference scale, taking equal distances along the axis of abscissa to represent equal luminance units in, say, millilamberts, and equal distances along the axis of ordinates to represent a unit number of just noticeably different steps in brightness, then the data points would not fall along a straight line of direct proportionality but rather on a curve of the sort shown in the upper part of Fig. 1. The relation between

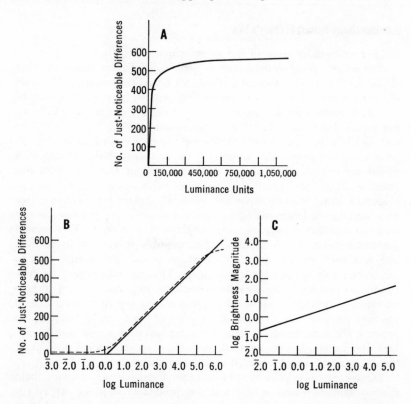

Figure 1. Relations between photometric luminance units and psychological scale units.

just-discriminable-brightness scale units and photometric stimulus units is a curvilinear one: the number of brightness steps increases rapidly with increase in number of luminance units at the low levels of luminance but only very slowly at the high luminance levels. The particular relation illustrated here becomes linear when we subject the photometric scale on the abscissa to a logarithmic transformation of the stimulus luminance units. This is shown in Fig. 1B. The linear relation between the scale of just-noticeable-brightness steps and the *logarithmic transform* of photometric stimulus luminance units is familiar in psychology, and this particular form of psychophysical relation is known as Fechner's law:

$$B = k \log L \tag{1}$$

where B is the brightness, L is the stimulus luminance, and k is a constant. Experimentally determined just-noticeable-difference scales tend to depart from Fechner's law at both the low and the high extremes of the stimulus dimension, but the proportionality between the number of just-noticeable differences and the logarithm of the stimulus values is usually found to hold fairly well for intermediate stimulus levels. The significance of the departures will be discussed in greater detail when the various problems of brightness discrimination are examined more closely.

The curve drawn as the dashed line in Fig. 1B illustrates an approximately logarithmic function of the sort that is actually found in such scaling experiments. Note that the scale units on the brightness ordinate have been chosen so that we have a total of between five and six hundred brightness steps between the minimal brightness that is visible at all and the maximal brightness that can be perceived. The total number of steps shown in this figure is representative of actual data and agrees with the early findings of A. König, a German psychophysicist who obtained quantitative data on a number of visual problems in the late nineteenth and early twentieth centuries.

Although we described the scaling experiment based on discriminability in terms of a continuously variable light source exposed in the test field, we could, in principle, have done the same experiment by using a fixed source of illumination and by allowing this fixed amount of light to fall on a series of paper surfaces whose reflectances vary from the least reflecting black paper that is available to a maximally reflecting white one. If the value of the illumination is constant, the differences in test field luminances, as measured with a photometer, are now determined by the differences in the percent reflectances of our paper samples. It is not uncommon in the visual literature to find visual stimuli of this sort specified in terms of their relative reflectances, and it is an adequate photometric specification provided, of course, that the constant illuminance value is also specified. The luminance range of test stimuli that can be obtained in this way is, however, severely limited. The best white paper never reflects as much as 100 percent of the light, which is the ideal maximum, and the most absorbent black paper usually reflects at least 1 percent of the incident light. Consequently, if the level of illumination provided by the light source is not also varied, then we are unlikely to obtain a luminance range of as great as 100 to 1 when the test stimuli are controlled only by means of their different reflectances. This means of stimulus variation, though convenient for many experiments, is therefore not very useful for discrimination scaling procedures.

Category Scales

Discrimination experiments, although classical, are by no means the only procedure for determining perceptual scales. One alternative technique is called category scaling. In this procedure, as used for example by Michels and Helson in 1949, we present to the observer a fairly large sample of achromatic papers of different reflectances and ask him to place each in turn in one of nine lightness categories. The category of samples described as "very, very dark" has the lowest number and the samples described as "very, very light" are assigned to the category with the highest number. Because of the necessarily limited number of categories, this procedure forces the observer to make his judgments in terms of much coarser units than the unit of discriminability. The theory underlying the use of such scaling procedures, however, assumes that limiting the number of categories serves only to reduce the precision of the measures, in much the same way that we could measure length less precisely if we had a ruler divided in inches than if we had one divided in fractions of inches. With the coarser ruler, we do not alter our scale of length in any essential way, but simply make a less precise measurement. In fact, however, there are more serious problems involved in the category scaling procedure, and these problems relate to stimulus sampling. One difficulty is thought to be caused by a tendency on the part of observers to use all the categories available to them in an experiment and moreover to make their judgments in such a way that approximately the same number of the total sample of stimuli will be assigned to each of the available categories.

We can easily see how this tendency could operate if we imagine two separate category scaling experiments carried out with two different sets of stimulus samples. We may suppose that one set contains a very large number of samples that appear relatively bright and only a small number that appear dark. In the other experiment the sampling is reversed: it includes a large number of samples that appear relatively dark and only a few that appear bright. The brightest and the darkest samples, respectively, will probably be placed in the extreme (highest and lowest) categories in both experiments. In the experiment where there are many light samples, however, the least bright of these will be distributed into lower category numbers than in the experiment which provides the observer with only a few of the brighter samples, and the reverse will be true for the other sample array. The reader will probably note that an experimenter would be unlikely to select test stimuli in either of these two ways, and indeed he will try not to do so except to demonstrate this very point about the effect of stimulus sampling. It must be remembered though, that in scaling experiments of this sort, there is no correct "answer" that is known a priori to the experimenter. If we knew in advance how bright each of the stimuli in the array actually looked to an observer, then the scaling experiment would no longer be an experiment but simply an exercise.

H. Helson, the American psychologist who is responsible for a large body of important research on visual problems and on problems of psychological scaling in general, has treated effects of this sort that are related to category scaling within the framework of his adaptation-level theory. Helson reasons that when an observer is confronted with an array of stimuli of different brightnesses, whether they are presented simultaneously or successively, and is asked to categorize them, what he does is to set up a middle, neutral category and partition other stimuli into two main groups above and below the level that he has selected as the neutral, "equilibrium" level. The stimulus value corresponding to this equilibrium level is determined by the observer's "adaptation-level" in the given situation. The adaptation-level itself is determined by all of the stimuli to which the observer is exposed in the situation, and it is equal to a specific weighted average of their individual luminance values. Consequently, the stimulus values corresponding to the adaptation-level will be higher when the array of test stimuli to be scaled includes a large number of brighter samples, and it will be lower when the stimulus array includes a relatively large number of darker samples. The background against which the individual test stimuli are judged is also part of what the observer sees in the experiment, and this background, as well as the array of test stimuli, enters as an important determinant of the adaptation-level. On the basis of separate experiments in which the same set of test stimuli were judged in a category scaling procedure when seen against three different backgrounds—high, low and intermediate reflectances, respectively—Michels and Helson developed a specific quantitative statement for the relation between apparent brightness and stimulus luminance that takes into account the effect on the judgments of the value of the adaptation-level. This expression is:

$$J = K \log X - K \log A. \qquad (2)$$

In this expression, J refers to the brightness judgments, X refers to the stimulus measures, in this case the stimulus luminances, and A represents the value of the adaptation-level. A is, as we said above, a weighted average value of all of the stimulus and background luminances involved in the observing situation. K is a constant and represents the slope of the function. Since the expression $(\log X - \log A)$ is equivalent to log (X/A), we see that the important relation is between the apparent brightness judgment and the *ratio* of each test stimulus to all of the other visual stimuli that affect the organism, rather than between apparent brightness and the test stimulus alone. This is a basic and important concept, especially with respect to the operation of the visual system, and we shall find it turning up repeatedly when we consider other specific problems of brightness perception.

We note that, again, the relation between the light stimulation, expressed as a ratio, and the apparent brightness as determined by the category scaling procedures is a logarithmic one. As a matter of fact, Helson describes the psychophysical relation given in the equation above as a modified form of Fechner's law. This logarithmic formulation differs from an earlier ratio formula developed in 1922 by Adams and Cobb, who also stressed the importance of adaptation-level on the visual brightness scale. Their formula which uses different symbols, is:

$$B = 10L/(L + L_b). \tag{3}$$

In this nonlogarithmic ratio formula B is the perceived brightness, L is the luminance of the test light, and L_b is the background luminance level to which the observer is adapted. The number 10 is equivalent to the K in the Michels-Helson formula, and this particular value simply means that the brightnesses are categorized on a ten-point scale.

A simple and ingenious experimental procedure for determining a category scale of perceived brightness was devised by S. M. Newhall and reported in 1950. The method as used by Newhall was to present, on a given background and under a given illumination, a so-called gray scale made up of a series of achromatic paper samples arranged in order of increasing reflectance. Newhall's gray scale actually included 12 steps of different reflectances. In addition to the series of test stimuli made up of the 12 different reflectance samples, the observer was also presented with the grid of a simple rectangular coordinate system, in which equal units laid out along the axis of abscissa represented the step numbers of the sample scale to be evaluated, and equal units laid out along the axis of ordinates represented the step numbers, from 0 to 10, of the perceived brightness scale. The observer's task was to adjust the locations of small space markers in the coordinate system to represent the apparent brightnesses of the samples of different reflectance relative to each other. The sample with lowest reflectance that appeared darkest, step number 1 of the stimulus scale, was located at the zero position of the perceptual scale, and sample number 12, the test sample with the highest reflectance, was located at the highest step of the perceptual scale at the ordinate value 10. The observer moved the adjustable markers to indicate the relative positions of all of the intermediate stimulus samples in terms of their apparent brightness with the two extremes located, as we have already said, at the extreme anchor points. In this procedure the observer is permitted to make preliminary adjustments, to reexamine the stimulus array, and to correct his preliminary adjustments of the markers until he is finally satisfied that the marker positions represent accurately the brightness differences between adjacent samples as he perceives them. This procedure is essentially a method of category scaling, and, as Newhall points out in reporting his results, the brightness function measured in this way will depend on the spacing of the stimulus samples, the total range of sample reflectances available, and so on. In fact, the procedure seems ideally suited for the laboratory exploration of the effects of such variables on category scales of psychological brightness. It should be remembered that in the experimental coordinate system, the units along the abscissa are entirely arbitrary and represent only the assigned numbers of the stimulus samples used in order of their increasing reflectances. After the judgments have been made the data can be plotted in terms of equal units along the abscissa that represent accurately the percent reflectances of the samples, the luminances of the samples, the logarithm of the sample luminances or some other transformation of the photometric values. The particular stimulus transformation that is most suitable for the particular perceptual scale values obtained under the given conditions of the experiment will result in a representation of the data as a function that most closely approximates a linear relation.

Fractionation Scales

The method of bisection is another procedure for establishing a perceptual scale, and it may be used when there is provision for a continuously variable stimulus that can be adjusted by the observer. In this procedure, we might, for example, present to the observer two stimuli of luminances that are at the two extremes of the stimulus continuum, one having the maximal luminance to be used in the series and the other having the minimal luminance of interest. The observer is instructed to adjust the variable luminance of a third stimulus until its brightness appears to be precisely midway between the brightnesses of the other two. This stimulus, which is judged to bisect the total brightness interval, is then presented with either the higher or lower of the other two, and the interval between them is again bisected by having the observer make the same kind of judgment and adjustment that was made in the first instance. Iteration of this procedure can be continued to produce division into progressively smaller intervals. Although the aim of the bisection or fractionation experiment is to establish a series of light stimuli that are equally spaced in terms of their apparent brightnesses, we can see that, if the total array of stimuli determines the perception, the equal brightness intervals that are produced in the separate observations should be expected to appear precisely equal only for a given triad of high, low, and bisection stimuli. For the first bisection judgment, the extreme members of the stimulus series and the variable stimulus, together with the fixed background, constitute the total array of stimuli that determine the adaptation-level. When the second bisection adjustment is made, the triad of stimuli is changed to include the middle stimulus determined from the first judgment, the same high luminance that was used for the first bisection, and a new intermediate stimulus. Obviously, for each iterated bisection judgment, there is a different value for the adaptation-level. This changing adaptation-level for each successive bisection judgment makes it difficult, indeed, to interpret the significance of the overall scale produced by this procedure. As we can see by the formula for the adaptation-level form of Fechner's law, for a scaling experiment in which the adaptation-level, and thus the value of log A, is constant, we would have a straight line relation between the scale of apparent brightness determined by the judgments J and the logarithm of the stimulus luminance, X. On repetition of the experiment with the same sample of test luminances but with the stimuli viewed against, say, a brighter background, the formula predicts a different function that would be displaced to lower ordinate values on the graph, but again the brightness would be linearly related to the logarithm of the stimulus luminance. If, however, the adaptation-level, and thus the value of log A, varies during the experiment from one value of the stimulus luminance X to the next, as in the bisection method, then each judgment locates the brightness of a point on a different one of the many functions associated with the many values of A.

Thus far, we have seen that Fechner's law, based on just-discriminably different steps in brightness, proposes that there is a logarithmic relation between apparent brightness and the photometric luminance of a light stimulus. Helson's scaling experiments resulted in a modification of this law to say that there is a logarithmic relation between apparent brightness and a ratio that expresses the luminance of the test stimulus relative to an average luminance of all stimuli that have an effect on the organism in a given situation. Can we at least be certain that the relation between perceived brightness and light stimulation is necessarily a logarithmic one? This general relation has itself been challenged off and on throughout the years, both on theoretical grounds and on the basis of experimental measures that are inconsistent with it, and we have already seen that Adams and Cobb had an earlier adaptation-level formulation much like Helson's except that it was a linear rather than a logarithmic one.

Magnitude Scales

Although scientific arguments against the logarithmic psychophysical relation have a long history, in recent years Fechner's logarithmic law has been challenged most forcefully by S. S. Stevens. The psychological scaling method advocated by Stevens involves the estimation of ratios of apparent brightnesses for stimuli of different luminances. In the procedure that he and his associates use most often, the judgments are numerical estimates of brightness magnitudes. To obtain such numerical estimates, some one light of given luminance is selected from the total series to be presented, and a specific number is assigned to the level, or magnitude, of apparent brightness that is produced by this "standard" stimulus. Each stimulus in the test series is then presented successively, usually in a more or less random order, and the observer assigns to each of the test lights a number that expresses the perceived brightness of the given test stimulus relative to that of the standard. Thus, if the standard is assigned, say, the number 10, then a test light that appears about three quarters as bright will be given the number 7.5, one that appears 10 times as bright will be called 100, and so on. Like the category scaling procedure, the method of magnitude estimation can be used with a large number of observers, and the judgments are fairly easy to make provided only that the individuals are sufficiently familiar with the number system to be able to estimate fractional relations and to convert them into a numerical estimate. Typically, the method has been used by Stevens and his associates to obtain group average or median estimates from large numbers of observers, although other investigators have also used the technique successfully by obtaining repeated judgments from small numbers of individuals. In the latter case, a large sample of different test luminances must be used if each repeated judgment is to be made independently of the preceding judgments of the same stimulus. When brightness magnitude estimations are made at a series of stimulus luminance levels for isolated stimulus fields that are exposed briefly in otherwise dark surroundings, then the psychophysical relation that is found between apparent brightness and stimulus luminance is not a logarithmic function. Nor is there a simple linear relation between the scale of perceived brightness and the scale of photometric luminance. Rather, it is found that, at least for moderately large test fields, apparent brightness increases directly with the cube-root of the stimulus luminance. $B = kL^{1/3}$, or in logarithmic form, $\log B = \log k + 0.33 \log L$. The general form of the psychophysical law that Stevens espouses for all psychological scales that relate perceptual magnitude in any sensory domain to intensive variations of the appropriate stimulus is:

$$P = kS^n. \tag{4}$$

Here P is the perceived magnitude, k is a constant, S is the stimulus amount in appropriate units, and n is a power that varies for different perceptual continua, for example, loudness, apparent weight, and so on. For the brightness scale, and for the stimulus conditions that we have specified above, the power n is equal to approximately 0.33. Figure 1C shows a scale of this form that can be compared with the graph shown in Fig. 1B to illustrate Fechner's law.

COMPARISON OF ALTERNATIVE FORMULATIONS

How are we to account for the different forms of the functions shown in Fig. 1, both of which presumably represent the relation between the stimulus scale and the scale of perceived brightness? One line of reasoning says that the magnitude estimates are ambiguous because we do not actually know how observers translate their perceptions into a number scale, which is, of course, the task required of them in the magnitude estimation procedure. If the observers do not actually do what it is assumed they do, namely, emit numbers that are directly related to the brightness levels that they perceive, then the magnitude estimation scales become unsuitable measures to determine the form of the psychophysical relation. If so, then we need not worry about the fact that magnitude scales do not agree with scales based on discrimination steps. If we look at the other side of the coin, however, do we have any justification for assuming that each step that is perceived to be just-perceptibly brighter than a preceding one is really 1 *unit* brighter in perceived magnitude? One could argue that each just-perceptibly brighter step represents a constant *percentage* increment over the preceding one rather than a constant *unit* increment. Fechner, of course, made the unit assumption which implies that the apparent brightness of a light stimulus is directly related to the cumulated number of just noticeable steps that this stimulus represents above the first step in the scale. But if, instead of the unit assumption, each successive *jnd* step is interpreted to mean that the stimulus appears, say, 1.1 times as bright as the preceding step rather than 1 unit brighter, then the *jnd* step scale must be multiplied by this constant factor at each level in order to convert numbers of *jnd*'s to brightness magnitudes. A multiplicative treatment based on such an assumption converts Fechner's logarithmic relation to a power relation of the sort that is obtained directly by the magnitude estimation procedure. This interpretation does indeed seem a reasonable one. It is also of some importance to remember that, in determining a scale of just-noticeable differences, experimenters often do not take precautions to exclude a systematically shifting adaptation level. If the observer becomes adapted to progressively higher luminance levels for successive measures of just-discriminable steps in brightness, then each step of the scale will be valid only for its own unique state of bright adaptation. Consequently, such logarithmically spaced scales depend strongly on the changing adaptation level. D. B. Judd of the U.S. National Bureau of Standards, who has much practical experience with the use of perceptual scales for applied industrial problems, says that the logarithmic relation "describes very satisfactorily a uniform lightness scale, provided that the visual appraisal of each small difference is made by an observer completely adapted to a luminance intermediate to those of the two grays defining the step."

It is also of some interest that one of the best known systems of color specification, the Munsell system, has an apparent lightness scale that is spaced in accordance with a power function as the psychophysical relation between apparent lightness and surface reflectance. When this system of color specification was first developed by A. H. Munsell, an artist and art teacher with a scientific bent, the Munsell color samples were spaced with lightness (called "value" in this system) increasing logarithmically in accordance with Fechner's law. However, as the original Munsell system has been modified throughout the years to improve the uniformity of the perceptual steps, the "value" spacing has been altered from the original logarithmic one to a power law form.

It would be misleading to imply, however, that this issue has really been settled in favor of the power law and against the logarithmic relation. Actually investigators will probably continue to devise experiments and cite theoretical reasons in favor of one or the other of these two basic relations for some time to come before any true resolution emerges. In any event, neither a simple logarithmic relation nor a simple power function will be adequate to describe all brightness scales for different background conditions and for different levels of adapting luminance.

There is, moreover, a fundamental aspect of the psychophysical relation between perceived brightness and stimulus luminance that we have not yet touched upon at all. In discussing different procedures, we have talked about producing test fields of different luminances by varying the intensity of a light source, and we have also mentioned luminance variations produced by varying the percent reflectance of a surface while the level of illumination falling on the surface is kept constant. The situation most typical of everyday life is still different. This situation is one in which we have an array of several surfaces of different reflectances, with this array of different reflectances seen under illuminations that also vary in level. Let us imagine such a case, where the array of objects in the observer's field of view and their reflectances remain constant, and their different luminances are increased proportionately by increasing the overall level of illumination. Suppose further that we start with no illumination at all and with the visual system in a dark-adapted condition. This situation might arise in everyday life if an individual were to awaken before dawn in a totally light-free room. None of the objects in the room will be visible, and the visual field will have an overall appearance that is best described as either "dim gray" or simply "dark." As dawn approaches and the objects of various reflectances begin to be feebly illuminated, different objects in the room begin to emerge more or less clearly from the background. At this state the appearances of the objects are best described as a series of grays of more or less dimness. If at this point, we were to illuminate the room fully, then as soon as we recovered from the sudden glare experience, we would see, for example, a telephone note pad clearly as a bright white pad, and the telephone itself would appear deep black. Thus, with the increase in illumination, the initially dim gray of the telephone pad increases to a bright white, but at the same time the initially somewhat dimmer gray of the telephone itself appears to change in the opposite direction to a much deeper black. If the telephone pad has a surface such that it reflects 90 percent of the incident illumination and the telephone itself only 1 percent, then these relative reflectance values are unchanged when the illumination is increased and the luminance, at the eye, of the light from both of these two objects must increase and both in the same proportion. Yet the apparent brightness moves in two opposite directions in the two instances. Consequently, if we are to have a psychophysical law that is truly general, it must be able not only to take into account the way that brightness units are related to units of luminance and the way that the brightness scale is modified with changes in adaptation level, it must also account for the variation of brightness in *two opposite directions* when the illumination change, and thus the variation in luminance, occurs in only a *single direction*. This capacity of the visual system to react to increases in stimulation in dual and opposed ways must be kept in mind if we are to understand many visual brightness phenomena, and it is a property to which we shall return again and again in succeeding chapters.

BIBLIOGRAPHY

ADAMS, E. Q., & COBB, P. W. The effect on foveal vision of bright (and dark) surroundings. *J. exp. Psychol.*, 1922, **5**, 39–45.

BURNHAM, R. W., HANES, R. M., & BARTELSON, C. J. *Color: A Guide to Basic Facts and Concepts.* New York: Wiley, 1963.

HELSON, H. *Adaptation-Level Theory.* New York: Harper, 1964.

JAMESON, D., & HURVICH, L. M. Perceived color and its dependence on focal, surrounding, and preceding stimulus variables. *J. opt. Soc. Amer.*, 1959, **49**, 890–898.

JAMESON, D., & HURVICH, L. M. Complexities of perceived brightness. *Science*, 1961, **133**, 174–179.

JUDD, D. B. *Color in Business, Science and Industry.* New York: Wiley, 1952. P. 226.

LEGRAND, Y. *Light, Colour and Vision.* (English Translation, R. V. G. Hunt, J. W. T. Walsh, & F. R. W. Hunt) London: Chapman and Hall, 1957. Chap. I, II, and IV.

MICHELS, W. C., & HELSON, H. A reformulation of the Fechner law in terms of adaptation-level applied to rating-scale data. *Amer. J. Psychol.*, 1949, **62**, 355–368.

MUNSELL, A. H. *A Color Notation.* (1st ed.) Boston: Ellis, 1905.

MUNSELL, A. H. A pigment color system and notation. *Amer. J. Psychol.*, 1912, 23, 236–244.

MUNSELL, A. H. *A Color Notation*. (9th ed.) Baltimore: Munsell Color Co., 1941.

NEWHALL, S. M. A method of evaluating the spacing of visual scales. *Amer. J. Psychol.*, 1950, 63, 221–228.

NEWHALL, S. M., NICKERSON, D., & JUDD, D. B. Final report of the OSA Subcommittee on the spacing of the Munsell Colors. *J. opt. Soc. Amer.*, 1943, 33, 385–418.

STEVENS, S. S. On the psychophysical law. *Psychol. Rev.*, 1957, 64, 153–181.

STEVENS, S. S., & GALANTER, E. Ratio scales and category scales for a dozen perceptual continua. *J. exp. Psychol.*, 1957, 54, 377–411.

STILES, W. S., & CRAWFORD, B. H. The luminous efficiency of rays entering the eye pupil at different points. *Proc. roy. Soc.*, 1933, B 112, 428–450.

TORGERSON, W. S. *Theory and Methods of Scaling*. New York: Wiley, 1958.

WALSH, J. W. T. Photometry. (2nd ed.) London: Constable, 1953.

II

Absolute Threshold of Vision

AT THE END OF THE PRECEDING CHAPTER we discussed awakening in the dark of night in a totally light-free room. Under such circumstances the objects in the room are not visible and the visual field is a dim gray or simply dark.

If instead of turning a light on, we continue to sit in the dark, preferably with eyes shut, a rather surprising thing is observed. We begin to see shifting clouds of "retinal light." These are floating light spots of various sorts; they have been described by many investigators and take many forms peculiar to the individual observer. They sometimes look like curved bands with dark intervals between them and they have also been described as cloud-like streamers and ribbons. Sometimes circular waves that contract and move towards the center in rhythmic cycling patterns have been reported. The overall background sometimes darkens and lightens uniformly. These effects have been given a variety of names including "light chaos," "light dust," "self-light," "intrinsic light," "idioretinal light," "intrinsic gray" and "intrinsic brightness or darkness." Recently the term "retinal noise" has become a favorite. There have even been attempts to measure the brightness of the retinal light, and one investigator concluded that it is comparable to the brightness of a white paper illuminated by one-half of the light intensity of the planet Venus at the height of its glow. Whether this is an accurate determination or not is unimportant. What is important is that if we awaken at night in a nearly dark room, particularly in a strange environment, and try to move about the room, the intrinsic retinal light swirls can be bright enough to be confused with very dimly illuminated real objects in the room.

The fact that we experience visual sensations in the complete absence of radiant energy—that is, with our eyes in a so-called resting state

—is a fact of major importance. And equally important is the fact that the visual experience is not one of blackness. Only with an increase in room illumination do we experience deep blacks as well as whites. As daybreak approaches or if we turn on a room lamp, the increase in illumination wipes out the basic gray experience of the rested eye while the brightness gamut simultaneously increases both in the dark and light directions: the writing pad gets white, the telephone itself black.

ABSOLUTE SENSITIVITY

Since the resting state of the eye can generate visual sensations of clouds, specks, ribbons, swirls, and the like that are sufficiently bright to interfere with our recognizing dim objects in the room, we may ask just how much external light does an object need to radiate or reflect in order to be perceived as just noticeably different from the internally generated "light chaos." Of course, no one would want this precise information to keep from bumping into chairs standing in unfamiliar positions in a strange hotel room. A simple 7-watt "nite-light" would do this trick. It is the visual scientist who would like to know how the visual mechanism works who has long been interested in the absolute stimulus threshold, namely the least amount of light detectable when the background is dark or nonilluminated. But the light detection problem also has practical relevance in our highly industrial and jet-propelled culture. Consider transportation alone. Every mode of motorized transportation, bus and automobile, subway, railroad, ship, and plane, is dependent both on lights which indicate and identify the vehicles themselves as well as on traffic control signals of all sorts. In all instances, there is night traffic, and in all instances, it is important that signals be recognized as quickly and as early as possible and hopefully without error. Failure to detect signals both soon enough and correctly have resulted in innumerable accidents in all modes of transportation. One can, of course, think of many other instances where questions about the eye's sensitivity to light have practical importance. Military situations, lighthouse signals, radar scopes for traffic control and meteorology, for example, all come to mind. Nor should we overlook the fact that most astronomers still depend on visual observations of the skies through telescopes despite the wide use of photography, rapid developments in radio astronomy, and now even the relaying of photographs of the surfaces of planets by means of television cameras mounted in space vehicles.

Astronomers were among the first who were concerned with the limits of the eye's sensitivity and they rated stars on an arbitrarily defined stellar magnitude scale that extends from 1 for the brightest stars to larger numbers for increasingly dimmer ones. Stars of magnitude 6 are said to be the dimmest that can usually be seen at night with the naked eye, although with special care those of 8.5 magnitude can still be seen. These amounts of light are very small and they become meaningful to nonastronomers only when it is pointed out that they are comparable to a candle flame seen at a distance of 10–25 miles, depending upon the atmospheric conditions. The eye is astonishingly sensitive and different authors have favorite illustrations to dramatize this fact. Asher asks us to visualize the number of eyes that could see a candle flame 10 miles away, that is, the number of eyes that could be arranged on the surface of a sphere with a radius of 10 miles. To calculate this number the surface area of the sphere (1200 square miles) is divided by the area of a dilated pupil ($\frac{1}{12}$ square inch). The number turns out to be 10^{14}; hence $\frac{1}{10}^{14}$, or one trillionth part of the light from a single candle, is enough to stimulate vision. How sensitive the eye is in energy terms will be discussed later in the chapter. We want first to describe an illustrative experiment designed to measure what has traditionally been called the absolute threshold. This will enable us to discuss the important variables that affect the threshold and that need to be controlled.

EXPERIMENTAL MEASUREMENT OF ABSOLUTE
VISUAL THRESHOLD

Stimulus Specification and Intensity Control

Let us use two small adjacent rooms for the experimental setup, with a small circular hole, say 2 inches in diameter, in the wall separating the rooms, and cover the hole with a piece of translucent diffusing glass or plastic. In one room, the back one, we place on an optical rail a light source, say, a 25-watt incandescent lamp, at some convenient distance from the circular cutout and allow the light to fall on the back side of the diffusing disk. Since we need to be able to vary the energy of the light source so that the luminance of the disk can be varied, it might seem that the simplest thing to do would be to place some sort of variable voltage transformer or device for increasing the resistance in the circuit with the lamp to change its light output. A simple idea, but in this case it is not advisable. As we decrease the voltage to the lamp, we notice that the appearance of the lamp gets increasingly yellow, then orange, and even red. As the voltage is raised again the lamp loses the red appearance, gets yellower, and finally more white. Since we want to measure the threshold for a fixed color quality—we shall see why somewhat later

—we need a control that will not change the "color temperature" (a measure of the light quality) of the lamp as we vary its intensity. This requirement is met somewhat better, although not perfectly, by so-called neutral density wedges. As a rule, these wedges are sandwiches made up of two strips of glass with carbon deposits held between them and the amount or density of carbon varies continuously over the 10 or so inches of the strips of glass. As denser portions of the wedge are inserted in front of the source, less light is transmitted. But, as with a voltage control, although to a much lesser extent, different wavelengths of light are selectively favored as the density of the wedge changes. As more dense portions of wedge are introduced between the light source and diffusing disk, the light passed through the disk becomes increasingly yellow. New types of wedges that use monomolecular layers of metal deposits or dyes in conjunction with carbon deposits do not show this defect to any serious extent. In any event, for visual experiments where spectral lights with narrow bands of wavelengths are used, properly calibrated wedges are the means par excellence for controlling light intensity. Pairs of polarizing light prisms may also be used to control light intensity. If both prisms are placed so that the planes of polarization are aligned in the same direction, there is maximal light transmission. If one of the pair is fixed and the second prism is rotated through a 90° angle to the first, no light is transmitted. In between these two extremes the amount of transmitted light depends on the relative orientation of the prisms. Such prisms are very expensive, but relatively inexpensive Polaroid filters can be used in the same way that the prisms are. Polaroid filters, however, absorb different wavelengths of light differentially, and thus we face selective light changes again when using ordinary broad band light sources.

Two ways to control light intensity without altering the wavelength distribution of the light stimulus are (1) to use a rotating episcotister or (2) to vary the size of an aperture stop. The episcotister is simply a device composed of two superposed, adjustable disks made up of alternate opaque and cutout sectors. Mounted on a motor, the disks are rapidly rotated so that no visible flicker is seen. The amount of light that passes through the episcotister depends upon the ratio of open to opaque sectors in the total disk, and this ratio can be varied by shifting the superposed sector disks relative to each other.

An adjustable iris diaphragm of the sort used in cameras can also be used as an intensity control. If this variable aperture is placed between the light source and the diffuser, or better still, next to a collimating lens that makes the light rays coming from the lamp towards the disk parallel, the light intensity will be increased or decreased as the iris diaphragm is varied in size, much as the natural pupil of the eye controls the level of retinal illuminance. A variant of the aperture type of control is obtained by using two superposed gratings made of alternate opaque and clear bars. The amount of transmitted light can be controlled by slipping one grating over the other to increase or decrease the total clear area. Discrete steps can be obtained by using a series of wire mesh or gauze screens of different gauges. If the screens are blackened, problems of selective reflection and transmission are minimized.

But the easiest way of all to vary the light intensity without changing the spectral light distribution is to place the lamp on an optical rail and simply move it nearer and farther from the diffusing field. For point sources of light, the so-called inverse square law of illumination will apply. The illuminance, the density of luminous flux on a surface, varies inversely with the square of the distance of the source from the surface. If we place a source twice as far from a screen as it has been, then the same luminous flux is now spread over four times as much area as before, thus its density is reduced to one fourth of what it was. If we place it at three times the original distance, it is spread over nine times as much area, its density is reduced to one ninth and so on. For lights that are larger than point sources, the drop-off in illumination with distance is somewhat slower. But we need not rely on the inverse square law to determine the illumination on the disk in our apparatus. We can use a calibrated photometer to measure the amount of light on the disk as the source is moved to different distances. The distance manipulation, used in conjunction with a series of neutral density filters or calibrated wire screens, provides an excellent yet simple control of intensity.

Sensitivity Changes with Time in Darkness

Since we now know how to control the stimulus intensity, let us return to the experiment. The observer is seated in the observation chamber a few feet from the diffusing disk. The room is darkened, and the experiment is under way. Provision has been made for two-way communication, and, having instructed the observer to signal when he sees the stimulus light first disappear, the experimenter starts to decrease the light energy falling on the disk. The observer signals the experimenter when he no longer sees the disk, and the experimenter records the lamp position on the optical rail as well as any filters or screens that have been placed in front of the lamp. But while the experimenter is busy recording the lamp distance, etc., the subject signals again that he sees the lighted disk—clear as a bell—to mix our metaphors. The experimenter consequently decreases the light intensity still more. When the observer signals again the experimenter starts to make another entry on his data sheet. But once more the observer reports that the light has become visible during the interval. What is happening, of course, is that the observer's sensitivity to light is increasing progressively as he continues his stay in the dark. If the experiment were continued even in this somewhat crude fashion for, say one hour, the threshold light intensity would continue to decrease. Measures of the threshold in luminance units could be plotted on the ordinate of a graph against time in the dark on the abscissa. The absolute threshold would decrease rapidly at first, then somewhat more slowly, and finally it would taper off to reach a fairly stable value after a half hour to an hour of repeated measurements.

The reason for our experiment was to determine the least amount of light that is perceptible when a person awakens in the dark of night. Since sensitivity increases with time in darkness, it is obvious that a person who has been asleep and has thus been shielded from light for many hours must have reached a high degree of visual sensitivity. Since we are not at the moment primarily concerned with the change in sensitivity in time, our experimental measures of the minimal amount of light perceived should begin only after the observer has remained in the dark for 45 minutes to one hour. By introducing this preliminary dark-adaptation period, a relatively stable equilibrium condition that approximates the condition of maximal sensitivity is assured.

Additional Stimulus Controls

Let us assume then, that the observer is left in the dark room for, say, 45 minutes. The experimenter could profitably take this time for an additional experimental provision. He should place an ammeter as well as some form of variable transformer in the lamp circuit to enable him to guarantee that the current flowing through the lamp remains fixed throughout the experiment. Adventitious line-voltage and current fluctuations and hence luminous flux changes would obviously contaminate the luminance threshold measures.

Retinal Location of Stimulus

The experiment gets under way again, the experimenter reduces the luminance gradually, and the disappearance of the disk is signalled. The procedure is repeated, and a series of measurements is taken. There is considerable scatter in the recorded values, and it occurs to the experimenter that there may be a serious flaw in his procedure. The observer has been kept in the dark for 45 minutes to reach a stable dark-adapted sensitivity level and has now also been instructed to keep his eyes closed between measurements. But each time the experimenter undertakes to determine the threshold he first exposes the observer to a brightly illuminated disk before he proceeds to gradually decrease its luminance. Is he not disturbing the dark-adapted equilibrium condition? He believes he is, and without further ado decides that in making his next measurements he will start somewhere far below the values he has already measured and gradually increase the light intensity. He moves his lamp back to the far end of the optical rail and asks the observer to open his eyes. Much to his astonishment, the observer says he sees the disk. The observer is asked to close his eyes, the experimenter checks the apparatus, the ammeter reading, the wire screen size, etc. Another "ready" signal is given. The observer opens his eyes and reports that he sees the test stimulus. E is puzzled and about to give up when O informs him that he too is puzzled. Although he saw the disk when he first opened his eyes, it was somewhat blurred and appeared off to the side. When he turned his eyes to look directly at it, it disappeared. As a matter of fact, he can make it disappear and reappear depending on whether he looks directly at it or off to one side. It suddenly dawns on the experimenter that he has heard of this before. When star gazing, one often sees faint stars appear only when the gaze is directed a bit away from them. When the test field was first exposed at a luminance level much higher than threshold, the observer's fixation was controlled. Now, when the luminance is first set at a level much lower than threshold, the observer has nothing to look at when he first opens his eyes, and some provision must be made to control the direction of his gaze. A fixation mark can be provided rather simply by reflecting a tiny spot of light from a clear slip of cover glass placed in front of the stimulus disk. By rotating the cover glass, the position of the fixation dot relative to the center of the disk can be varied, and in this way the image of the disk can be projected on different parts of the retina. Since the observer seemed to be more sensitive at a parafoveal (off-center) retinal locus, the fixation dot is now arranged so that the stimulus field falls at, say, 10° from the fovea. The fovea, we remember, is a small central area of the retina, about 1° in diameter, and it contains what are histologically defined as the cone elements.

Stimulus Size

We have spent a good deal of time now and have not really gotten far off the ground. Nor, for that matter, are we out of the woods yet. Since we have now arranged to stimulate the eye at 10° from the fovea, on a part of the peripheral retina where there is a high proportion of the retinal receptor elements known as rods, and where the observer has shown himself to be highly sensitive, the experimenter introduces an additional wire screen to further cut the light on the diffusing disk. He starts the light exposure below the threshold—the observer now has no difficulty maintaining his fixation—and when the light is first seen, the observer signals. As he relaxes back into his chair, just prior to closing his eyes, however, the observer is surprised to see that the light disappears. With his eyes still focussed on the fixation mark he moves forward, and he sees the stimulus field reappear. He so informs the experimenter over the intercom, and still another problem needs to be resolved. A few more quick checks and it becomes obvious that the size of the stimulus field is an important variable and that forward and backward movements of the observer have to be eliminated. This can be done by mounting a commerically available head and chin rest of the sort used by ophthalmologists on a table in front of the observer. Or we can have the observer make a dental impression in a wax-covered biting-board which provides a rigid support for the observer's head at whatever fixed distance it is placed from the stimulus field. The conventional way of changing stimulus size is not, of course, to move the observer back and forth but rather to change the size of the opening in front of the diffusing glass.

Exposure Time

To measure the least amount of light that can be seen seems to be a complicated and tricky business. We have an accurately specifiable stimulus source (in color temperature terms) whose light output is well regulated; we have pretty good control of the basic sensitivity level since the observer is fully dark-adapted when the measurements start; we know fairly precisely where the stimulus is imaged on the retina despite the fact that small eye movements of various sorts—flicks, saccades, drifts—are not easily eliminated; and we can specify rigorously the stimulus size. Still, our observer reports that he continues to have difficulty in making a decision whether he sees the light patch or not. The experimenter assures him that he need not be troubled by the fact that the disk is not always seen clearly outlined and defined. Peripherally fixated objects are always more fuzzy than those seen centrally with the fovea. The fovea is the area we use for sharp vision, and our acuity here is best. But fuzziness is not the observer's complaint. He has been using as his so-called "criterion response" the first appearance of any light regardless of its form or sharpness. What does trouble him is that just as he signals, "Yes, I see it," the spot of light seems to disappear. As he continues to hold his fixation·it sometimes reappears then fades out again. More discussion between observer and experimenter and it is agreed that all is not well yet. Shall the observer wait until the light is clearly present at all times before signaling? Would this be a valid threshold measurement—a determination of a barely visible light? Should they return to the "descending method" of light variation in spite of all the difficulties it creates in connection with adaptation level and report the point of first definite disappearance of the light? This would give a measure of a luminance that is never seen as contrasted with the ascending measure which records a value that is always definitely seen. Probably both values should be averaged. Maybe the stimulus should be exposed for a limited time rather than continuously until the observer makes his report.

Suppose the retina behaves like a photographic plate. As we know, a photographic plate has storage capacity. If the time exposure is very brief, the film may not be able to record the light from a faint star, but if we permit the light to remain on it long enough, we get an image of the star. This is strictly in accordance with the Bunsen-Roscoe law which states that $i \times t = k$, and thus increased time can compensate for weak intensity. In our visual experiment, by exposing the observer's eye continuously as we increase the light intensity up to "threshold," we may be obtaining a deceptively low luminance measure. If the Bunsen-Roscoe law were valid for vision, the longer the exposure, the less the stimulus energy necessary to see it. The law does not hold for vision for long stimulus durations, but the eye does store energy over time for very short exposure times. Thus the notion to control exposure time is basically a sound one, and with the introduction of a photographic shutter (or a pendulum) to limit the stimulus duration to some fixed value, we now have the important variables all under control. When we turn to the use of very brief stimulus flashes we must remember to run our light sources on direct current to avoid the light fluctuations produced by alternating currents.

Method

The use of stimulus flashes of short duration raises a new series of questions related to the measurement of the threshold. In the method of limits with continuous variation and continuous viewing the stimulus is started either at an initially nonvisible value and gradually increased until it is *just perceptible* or started at a clearly visible value and gradually decreased in intensity until it is *just not perceptible.* The observer can signal at precisely the moment when the criterion is reached.

But since we now present each stimulus as an individual flash at some fixed level of luminance, how do we decide exactly where the threshold lies? Some flashes are always perceived, others are never seen. The threshold level presumably lies between. The way out seems obvious. By using a series of stimulus flashes at different luminance levels, we can measure the frequency with which each luminance is reported as seen in a long series of repeated exposures. The experimenter selects 5 to 7 stimuli, the highest of which nearly always produces a "yes" or positive response, and the lowest only rarely evokes a "yes" response. The stimuli are exposed in a random sequence for a total of, say, 100 presentations each. The frequency of "yes" responses to each stimulus is plotted on the ordinate against stimulus luminance on the abscissa. This produces an ascending curve which is called the "frequency-of-seeing" curve. The threshold or critical stimulus level can be arbitrarily specified as that luminance which generates a response "seen" with a frequency of, say, 50 percent. This is the stimulus value which is just as likely to be seen as not. Since it is extremely improbable that a luminance has been selected that produces precisely a "50 percent seen" value, this point is either calculated or more usually read from the graph by interpolating between the two luminances on the two sides of the 50 percent threshold point. Plots of log stimulus luminance against frequency of "seen" responses on probability paper tend to produce straight-line functions which facilitate interpolation. Reciprocal slope values of these functions are also direct measures of the variability of the threshold measure.

Visual scientists have relied extensively on the threshold data to determine various properties and capacities of the eye and to evaluate the many theories that have been proposed to explain how it works. Hundreds of studies have been undertaken to show the way the absolute threshold is influenced by changes in the variables we have mentioned in our hypothetical experiment. Let us now look more closely at some of these variables.

EXPERIMENTAL DATA

Retinal Location of Test Field

Measurements of the absolute threshold made with a small white test field, say 4' or 20' in angular size, show that sensitivity is lowest at the fovea itself and increases very rapidly out to about 10° or so in the periphery along a given meridian. Sensitivity then tapers off somewhat, and finally becomes very low again at the extreme periphery (about 80°).

The most obvious place to look for the basis of these sensitivity variations is in the anatomical structure of the retina itself. There are two types of receptor elements in the human eye which are differentiated on the basis of anatomical characteristics as rods and cones. These two populations of receptors are distributed differently in the retina. The cone elements are densely packed in the fovea where there are few if any rods, and their numbers drop off very quickly towards the periphery. The rod population starts just outside the central foveal area which is about 1° in angular size. There are relatively few rods near the fovea but their numbers rise rapidly to a maximum at 16° or so, and then they too begin to drop off in number.

The Duplicity (or Duplexity) theory assumes that different visual functions are to be assigned to the activity of one or the other of the two groups of receptor elements. The rods are presumably better adapted for night vision and so-called scotopic functions are assigned to their activity. The cones are presumed to function in daylight and at relatively high luminance levels, and so-called photopic functions are carried out by their action. The dark-adapted threshold is assumed to be a manifestation of rod activity, and thus the change in sensitivity with change in retinal location is presumably explained by the distribution of the rod elements in the retina. However, the way in which the absolute threshold varies with angular distance from the fovea bears no one-to-one relation with the way the rods are distributed. It is important to remember when making such comparisons that not only are the different receptor elements present in different numbers at different locations, but the specific paths over which excitation is transmitted from the primary receptor cells to the visual cortex over the intermediate bipolar and ganglion cells in the retina also differ. In general, the secondary or collector neurons tend to decrease in density as we go from the fovea to the periphery. The density of the optic nerve fibers associated with ganglion cells also decreases in the same way. It seems obvious that all of these structural differences enter in the variation of the absolute threshold with retinal location.

However, another way in which the rod-cone dichotomy influences threshold measures in different parts of the retina relates to the different sensitivities of the two kinds of elements to different wavelengths of light. Thus, if instead of using white light, retinal sensitivity is tested with stimulus lights of different wavelengths, we find that the threshold varies with retinal location in different ways for the different wavelengths. For 580 nm, 475 nm, and 435 nm sensitivity is minimal at the foveal center as it is for white light and increases toward the near periphery. The increase is especially marked for short wavelengths, so that for 435 nm at 12° in the nasal direction, sensitivity is increased relative to the fovea by as much as 2.5 logarithmic units. With red light (700 nm) on the other hand, sensitivity is maximal at the fovea and then decreases somewhat at about 2.5° from the center. If we look directly at a small very dim blue light it is not seen unless we turn our gaze aside to view it peripherally. Since sensitivity varies in the reverse way for reddish lights, they are favored for fixation marks in visual experiments.

Stimulus Size; Ricco's Law; Piper's Law

The dimensions of the test field critically affect the luminance necessary for a threshold response, and, not surprisingly, an increase in the size of the test stimulus makes it possible to decrease its luminance for minimal perceptibility. Conversely, a decrease in the size of the stimulated area requires that the luminance be raised in order for the test field to be seen. Experiments on this variable date back to the last century, and it has long been accepted that for measures in the fovea the product of luminance times area is constant at threshold. This means that however the light may be distributed spatially, threshold is reached for a constant luminous flux. Another way to phrase it is to say that sensitivity is directly proportional to stimulated area, and that complete spatial summation takes place in the foveal part of the retina. This generalization about the equivalence of luminance and area in visual stimulation is called Ricco's law. It is written as

$$L \times A^n = C,$$ (1)

where the exponent n is equal to unity. It is now believed that the retinal region throughout which this perfect reciprocity holds is actually only a fraction of the entire fovea, perhaps as small as an angular subtense of only about 10'.

A different relation is usually associated with the periphery of the eye. Here are some illustrative results for the dark-adapted periphery:

Area (relative units)	Luminance at Threshold (relative units)	Product of Area × Luminance	$\sqrt{\text{Area}}$	Product of $\sqrt{\text{Area}}$ × Luminance
1	10.0	10.0	1	10
10	2.94	29.4	3.16	9.3
25	1.96	49.0	5	9.8
100	1.02	102	10	10.2

We see from the table that the product of area times luminance is far from constant, but that the product of square root of area times luminance is nearly so:

$$L \times A^n = C,$$ (2)

where the exponent n is equal to 0.5. This relation is known as Piper's law. Sensitivity in this case is proportional to the square root of area. Piper reported it to be valid for extra-foveal fields varying from about $3°$ to $26°$ in diameter.

Empirical relations of the sort expressed by Ricco's law and Piper's law are important in setting the stage for explanations which will account for the different degrees of summation—that is, the extent to which increases in stimulus area can effectively substitute for increases in stimulus luminance in order to get enough light to generate a visual signal. Some investigators believe that there is a transition from Ricco's law to Piper's law as we move from fovea to periphery. Others believe that for any given retinal location there is a transition from Ricco's to Piper's law with increase in stimulus area beyond very small field sizes. For example, at $30°$ in the periphery, for very small test fields less than 30', it is reported that the summation index is also unity; that is, the exponent $n = 1$ just as it is for small foveal fields. And in the fovea for test fields between 10′ and 1°, Piéron finds that summation is not perfect; the exponent n varies between 0.3 and 0.5, and the relation is

$$L \times A^{0.3} = C \tag{3}$$

or

$$L \times A^{0.5} = C \tag{4}$$

which, of course, approximates the peripheral result expressed in Piper's law. But the problem is a complex one particularly if variations in time of exposure and adaptation state are also introduced in the different experiments.

Whatever the specific "law" may be, it is clear that, within certain size limits and for certain stated conditions, an increase in the area of stimulation makes it possible to decrease the test luminance for threshold. Adjacent retinal areas seem to cooperate to produce a light response. But suppose we change the way in which we increase the area of retina stimulated. Let us now use two small semicircular test patches side by side instead of one homogeneous test area. Presenting the stimulus pattern in this way will, of course, show summative effects, but as we separate the two small half-disks, the degree of summation decreases. In fact, if the stimulus levels differ in the two parts of the bipartite field we may not only fail to find any summative effect at all, we even begin to see an opposite, inhibitory effect. Adjacent stimulation may make a small stimulated area look darker rather than brighter. We shall consider such inhibitory effects more closely in the following chapter on differential sensitivity.

Stimulus Duration; Bloch's Law

The time variable also enters as an important determinant of the absolute threshold. Exposure time and luminance, like area and luminance, are related in a reciprocal fashion, and, regardless of how short we make the stimulus duration, the luminance level can be raised sufficiently to compensate for the shortened time so that a threshold visual response occurs. We remember that the Bunsen-Roscoe law, which applies to the photochemical reactions of photography, states that intensity × time = C. In vision, it holds only over a range of relatively short stimulus durations. Depending on other experimental conditions, such as stimulus area and region of retina stimulated, the eye integrates or summates perfectly for durations up to about one tenth of a second.

$$L \times T^m = C \tag{5}$$

where the exponent m is equal to one (Bloch's law). For these short times what counts is the total quantity of light energy (the product of luminous flux and time) that strikes the retinal surface and not the way it is distributed in time. For exposure durations as long as, say, one second or more, temporal summation does not occur and for such durations, lengthening the exposure does not decrease the luminance required for threshold visibility. For intermediate durations, summative effects occur but summation is incomplete. Instead of finding that the product of luminance and time is constant at threshold as it is for extremely short light exposures, the data show that the value of this product increases with the somewhat longer exposure times. For these intermediate stimulus durations, the exponent m in the relation

$$L \times T^m = C \qquad (6)$$

is less than unity. The situation of temporal summation is thus much like that for spatial summation. Furthermore, the value of the exponent m seems to depend both on the part of the retina stimulated and on the size of the stimulus field. To express the facts of both temporal integration and spatial summation we may write the general formula

$$L \times T^m \times A^n = C. \qquad (7)$$

If we are using very brief flashes (say, 0.1 sec. in duration) of very tiny spots of light (say, 10′ angular subtense) which our observer is looking at directly, this formula tells us that the threshold will be determined by the total quantity of light integrated over space and time. If we double the luminance, we can compensate exactly for the luminance change by halving either the exposure duration or the test field size and again have a stimulus that is precisely at the threshold of visibility. Can we do the same thing by reducing the luminance to one tenth of the original threshold value and increasing either the stimulus duration or its size tenfold? Why not?

There is a direct analog in the temporal dimension to the summative effect shown when two test stimuli are spatially separated on the retina. If we present successively on the same part of the retina two very brief subthreshold flashes—that is, two stimuli which cannot be seen when each is presented alone—the two together can become perceptible because of the persistence of the first exposure. As with the spatial effect, the degree of temporal summation decreases as the two stimulus flashes are separated in time, but surprisingly some addition can still occur for intervals between the two flashes which are as long as 2 to 3 seconds.

One can introduce an additional variation in this experiment by exposing the two brief flashes successively and also at separate retinal positions. Two semicircular test fields may be separated by a small distance, say, by 20′ of arc, and the luminance threshold can be measured for the two successive flashes presented with varying time intervals between them. In such experiments it has been found that there is some summation over the stated stimulus separations for time intervals up to about 0.1 second between the two flashes.

We have said that spatially separated stimulations show summative effects which can also become antagonistic or inhibitory ones; the temporal variable shows similar properties. The experimental variation just cited which demonstrates that there is integrative action over the combination of space and time also manifests inhibitory effects. A stimulus which is separate in time and spatial position from another one can produce a complementary or facilitative effect, but it can also act in an antagonistic fashion. When the latter occurs the test stimulus can be made invisible and more light is required for its perception. We have emphasized the summative aspects as they relate to the absolute threshold; the antagonistic interactions are discussed more fully in a later chapter concerned with a variety of temporal effects on perceived brightness and darkness.

Monocular and Binocular Stimulation

In discussing the summative capacities of the eye in producing a threshold response we looked at different ways of adding stimulation—at adjacent parts of the retina or at successive moments in time on the same part of the retina. What if we added stimulation by exposing two eyes rather than one to the test flashes? Is the performance better with two eyes? Certainly we would not expect light detection to get worse but is there any evidence of summation? The dark-adapted absolute threshold is indeed found to be better with two eyes than with one. Some investigators claim that the summation is complete and that the test luminance for a binocular threshold is one half that of the monocular one. But this is a somewhat controversial question and most research indicates that the luminance threshold for two eyes relative to that for one eye is in a ratio of 1 to 1.4 and not 1 to 2. This degree of summation turns out to be essentially the same as Piper's law $(L \times A^{0.5} = C)$ for the variation in threshold luminance with increase in stimulus area: stimulating two eyes is equivalent to doubling the stimulated area in one eye. If a unit area is doubled so that

$$L_1 \times 1^{0.5} = L_2 \times 2^{0.5} = C, \tag{8}$$

the luminances L_2 to L_1 must be in the ratio of 1 to $2^{0.5}$ or 1 to 1.4 for a constant threshold effect.

Summative effects in one eye are ordinarily assumed to result from a pooling of physiological excitations at some level or levels in the visual pathways. Does the superior performance of two eyes over one also mean that there is pooling of the excitations from the two separate eyes? It can be argued that this is not so, but simply that in the two eye situation the probability of detecting the excitatory event necessary for threshold perception is increased in the way that it would be if we had two observers, each of whom was using only one of his eyes in the test situation. Suppose the test stimulus luminance is such that each observer detects only 50 flashes out of 100 that are presented. For either observer alone, this luminance value would represent the threshold level. Two observers exposed to the same flashes simultaneously but independently are likely to give positive reports for different individual flashes, however, and thus the total number of flashes seen will increase. In tossing a single coin, the probability of getting heads is one half; the probability of getting at least one head is increased to three quarters when two coins are used. Similarly if the two eyes of a given observer are assumed to be independent of each other, probability considerations alone predict the relative superiority of binocular over monocular stimulus detection.

Whether the lower threshold for binocular viewing is to be explained by statistical probability or by physiological summation depends crucially on the validity of the assumption that excitations from the two eyes are independent events. Many facts of binocular vision argue strongly against such an independence assumption, and hence the threshold analysis still remains open to question.

Test Stimulus Wavelength; Purkinje Shift and Adaptation

When the control of light intensity was discussed in describing the illustrative experiment, we said that we wanted to measure the absolute threshold for a fixed color quality of the light stimulus. The reason for this becomes clear if we determine the absolute threshold for a series of spectral lights of different wavelengths. Such measures yield a relative spectral sensitivity curve such as Curve A in Fig. 2. Sensitivity is represented as the reciprocal of the threshold energy value at each wavelength and is plotted here in logarithmic units. It should be noted that although the wavelengths differ, all of the stimuli appear as colorless flashes at threshold. These measurements for the dark-adapted, scotopic state are typically obtained at some peripheral retinal position where, we remember, the density of rod receptor elements in the retina is relatively high.

What if we measure the absolute energy level necessary to first detect a light stimulus presented at the fovea and when the eye is also kept bright-adapted and thus remains in the so-called photopic condition? The relative spectral sensitivity function measured under such conditions is shown as Curve B in Fig. 2. Throughout most of the spectrum the energy level required to first perceive a light flash is higher (sensitivity is lower) for photopic vision than it is in the dark-adapted or scotopic condition (Curve A). The energy difference, however, is

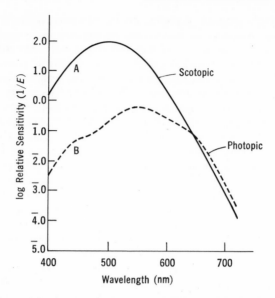

Figure 2. Spectral luminosity functions for scotopic and photopic conditions.

smaller at the longer wavelengths than it is elsewhere in the spectrum. These two functions are called luminosity functions, and they are sometimes taken to represent the way in which brightness varies with wavelength for an equal energy spectrum for the two different states of adaptation. Actually they do not represent brightness variations at all. What they do show is the way the energy (or its reciprocal $1/E$) varies at different spectral loci for the production of an equivalent threshold brightness.

Since these curves represent the different amounts of energy at different wavelengths that are required to produce a threshold brightness effect, they are of fundamental importance for relating photometric luminance units (millilamberts, candles per square meter, and so forth) to units of radiant energy (watts per steradian per square meter, and so forth). As we pointed out in Chapter I, conversion from radiant energy measures to photometric units is based on the visual effectiveness of a part of the total electromagnetic spectrum, and the luminosity function specifies what may also be called the relative visibility of different wavelengths within this restricted region of the total energy spectrum. Clearly the conversion is not the same for different states of bright- and dark-adaptation and, unless otherwise specified, standard photometric luminance units are based on the photopic, bright-adapted, luminosity function.

The bright-adapted "daylight" curve presumably reflects the action of the cone elements in the foveal center, the dark-adapted "night vision" function, the action of the rod elements. Intermediate curves represent the mesopic state of adaptation or "twilight" condition when mixed rod and cone activity presumably occurs. The relative effectiveness of the same spectral light varies with adaptive state. The luminosity curves for the photopic and scotopic conditions peak at two different spectral positions separated by about 50 to 60 nm. The displacement of these curves relative to one another is frequently described as the "Purkinje shift" and is related to a phenomenon known as the Purkinje effect. The eminent Czech physiologist, Purkinje, noted (1825) that at twilight or dawn the relative brightnesses of reds and blues as seen in daylight changes. When twilight begins to set in the brighter reds of daylight become considerably darker than the blues. One can observe this change particularly in paintings or by noting carefully the way the many colored objects of our everyday lives change in relative brightness towards evening or with the approach of sunrise.

A very common error in explaining the Purkinje shift is to link the effect to changes in stimulus intensity. Reds are said to be brighter than blues at high levels of intensity and darker than blues at low levels. Stimulus intensity, however, is not the critical factor. It is the adaptation level or organismic state that primarily determines the relative brightnesses of the stimuli, and stimulus intensity is relevant only to the extent that it enters as a factor in changing the adaptive state.

The primary importance of adaptation rather than stimulus luminance can be demonstrated in a simple pair of experiments with a double room setup that permits independent control of the two variables. We place a red and a blue filter respectively over each of two small apertures cut in the wall of the room in which the observer is seated. The apertures are independently illuminated by two separate lights placed behind them in the second room. The overhead illumination in the observer's room is used to control the adaptive state separately from the stimulus intensity of the two colored test stimuli. First, with the illumination high in the observer's room to keep him in a bright, or photopic, state of adaptation the observer equates the two colored stimuli in brightness at a moderately low brightness level, by adjusting their relative light intensities. The adaptation level is then lowered by reducing the overhead illumination in the observer's room. Although the relative intensities of the two colored stimuli remain unchanged, the blue appears to become brighter than the red. Let us do the converse experiment. Once again we start with a high adaptation level and with the red and blue stimuli matched in brightness. This time the overhead illumination in the observer's room is not changed but both the red and blue stimuli are decreased equally to a lower level of intensity. Now both stimuli

appear less bright, but there is no change in their relative brightnesses. In spite of the decrease in stimulus intensity, as long as the adaptation level remains unchanged, the red and blue fields continue to appear equally bright.

MINIMAL RADIANT ENERGY NECESSARY TO EXCITE
A VISUAL RESPONSE; QUANTUM MEASURES;
STIMULUS VARIABILITY

Our question at the beginning of this chapter concerned the smallest amount of light that an observer is able to detect. We have seen that many variables including region of the retina stimulated, size of test field, duration of exposure, wavelength of light, and state of adaptation all influence the amount of light required in order to perceive a test flash. Obviously there is no unique answer to the question as we have stated it thus far. One can, however, ask a different, but related question, namely, how little radiant energy will suffice to excite a retinal receptor in order to generate a visual signal? To determine this minimal amount of energy, it is, of course, necessary to select a set of conditions for which the visual system is maximally efficient in utilizing the incident light. These conditions might include full dark adaptation, a test area 10′ in visual angle located at 20° from the foveal center, time exposures of 0.001 second and radiant energy of 510 nm. The conditions cited are those selected by Hecht, Shlaer, and Pirenne in a study that many regard as classic.

The results of their experiment showed that, for seven observers, the threshold light energy lay between 2.1 and 5.7×10^{-10} erg. Since energy is emitted and absorbed in discrete packets—indivisible units called quanta —it is of interest to determine how many light quanta hit the visual receptors under these circumstances. The energy (hv) of a single quantum emitted at 510 nm is known to be 3.84×10^{-12} erg, and thus the threshold energies for these observers range between 54 and 148 quanta.

The values represent the number of quanta incident at the cornea, the transparent outer surface of the eye in front of the pupil. Before the light reaches the retina, however, it must pass also through the lens of the eye and the aqueous and vitreous humors which lie respectively in front of and behind the lens. If corrections are applied to take care of the light losses in the various eye media (4 percent reflection loss at the cornea, 50 percent absorption by media and lens at 510 nm) then only 26 of the 54 original quanta reach the surface of the retina. Hecht and his co-workers further assumed that only 20 percent of the 510 nm light at the retina is actually absorbed by the visual purple in the rod cells, and concluded that as few as 5 to 14 quanta are absorbed by the retinal cells when a light flash is seen under the described circumstances.

Since Einstein's photochemical equivalence law says that each quantum changes a single molecule of visual purple, it follows that to see a just-detectable flash of light only one molecule of visual purple in each of 5 to 14 rod cells needs to be transformed photochemically. The chemical transformation that takes place in the rods is assumed, of course, to stimulate nervous impulses, and these in turn are transmitted to the visual area of the cortex.

Other investigators have sought to determine these threshold quantum values with greater precision, and some have concluded that only a single quantum absorbed by a single rod can give rise to a visual sensation! Whether the minimal number of quanta necessary for a threshold visual response is 5, 14, or only 1, it is clear that the number is very small indeed. And this finding brings us to a consideration of the light source itself and the possible influence its own physical variation can have on threshold visual perception. A radiant source does, of course, show some variation in the number of light quanta that it emits from one moment to the next. At ordinary levels of seeing, this variation in physical emission is not large enough to be of any significance. But what of a threshold experiment where the observer is presented with a series of 100 flashes at a very low level of energy and reports that he sees only 50 of them? We can take this energy level as his threshold and determine the average number of quanta that it represents. But the number of quanta actually emitted in any one trial is sometimes slightly less, sometimes slightly more than the average, in accordance with accepted probability considerations. And since the average number is so small, it can be argued that this variation in stimulus energy determines the variation in visibility from one flash to the next rather than momentary fluctuations in the observer's own physiological state. By increasing the average intensity level, we increase the probability that a given flash will deliver at least the minimal number of quanta required for vision, and the frequency of "yes" responses at this level will simply reflect this increased probability. According to this kind of analysis, the frequency-of-seeing curve is really a measure of the physical variation of the stimulus in delivering at least a certain number of quanta which is itself invariant for a threshold visual response.

ORGANISM VARIABILITY

Is stimulus variability the only source of variation responsible for threshold fluctuations? At the beginning of this chapter we described a variety of changing visual experiences that occur in total darkness. "Light chaos," "intrinsic light," "visual noise," and so on are all reported in the complete absence of external light stimuli. These experiences reflect the spontaneous activity of the nervous system and attest to a basic, intrinsic biological variability. These biological fluctuations, as well as the random fluctuations in quantum light emission, can and do affect the threshold determinations. Furthermore, we should not overlook the relevance of the observer's response criterion and his motivation in the experimental situation.

Traditional Psychophysics

Traditionally, threshold experiments of the sort we have been discussing were carried out only after a series of training sessions in the experimental situation. During the training sessions, the observer became familiar with the task, developed some skill at maintaining his attention and fixation, and the experimenter was able to assure himself that the observer was reporting reliably what he saw and that he was not just wildly guessing. The experimenter does not, of course, know at what luminance level the observer's threshold may lie, and hence he cannot know in advance which stimulus flashes the observer really sees and which he may be falsely reporting or guessing to have occurred. He can, however, intersperse a number of trials in which, unknown to the observer, there is no stimulus exposure at all. The extent to which the observer is only guessing is then revealed by the frequency with which he gives "yes" responses to these blank trials in which no light stimulus was actually presented. The traditional psychophysicist judged the observer's motivational set and concentration on the task to be adequate only after he had achieved a low frequency of "errors" or false reports to such blank, or "catch" trials. This kind of procedure can obviously guarantee that the observer's guessing rate is low, and that his criterion for a report of "seen" is sufficiently high so that erroneously low threshold determinations will be avoided. Moreover, much reliable information and reproducible data have been obtained by following the traditional observer-training procedures.

Signal Detection

There is, however, a difficulty even here. Granted that a low guessing rate signifies an attentive, careful observer who will make few, if any, errors when there is no light stimulus present, how many "errors" of the opposite sort does he make? How many flashes does he see and yet fail to report? A low guessing rate to blank trials tells us nothing about this, and in recent years experimenters interested in signal detection have validly emphasized that it is just as important to know an observer's error rate in failing to report a signal as his "false alarm" rate. If an observer is motivated to avoid "false alarms," he can best do so by saying "no" to any very dim flash about which he is not absolutely certain, and this strategy will result in his "missing" a number of signals that he could have detected had he not been "overcautious." It has, in fact, been argued that the traditional approach does lead to such a state of affairs and that it consequently fails to give a true picture of the observer's capacity for signal detection.

In recent years the classical absolute threshold experiment has been vigorously challenged, and it is claimed that a better picture of an observer's sensory capacity is gained by analyzing variations in his response behavior rather than by trying to fix it in the traditional way. One of the basic tenets is that sensory excitation is continuous and there is no fixed sensory threshold but only different probabilities of *detecting* a signal. These probabilities depend not only on the strength of the stimulus signal but also strongly on the observer's response characteristics. Signal-detection theorists and theorists of human choice behavior have consequently sought to manipulate and analyze the observer's response criteria. By controlling the frequencies of presentation of signals (of fixed intensity) and of blanks, they can manipulate the observer's expectations about the likelihood of stimulus presentations. By controlling the system of rewards and penalties ("payoffs"), for "false alarms" ("yes" response when no stimulus is presented) and for "hits" or correct detections ("yes" response when stimulus is presented) they can manipulate the observer's motivation to avoid one kind of error or the other. From such experiments, the signal detection theorist determines what he calls the "receiver operating characteristic" (a representation of the observer's response biases) for different situations. For a fixed sensitivity condition the observer can manifest different "operating characteristics" depending on his cutoff points for making one kind of judgment (false alarm) versus another (hits). Presumably, this kind of analysis of response behavior will ultimately make it possible to make valid and precise corrections for an observer's response bias in a standard threshold experiment and thus to determine more accurately the minimal stimulus values to which his sensory system can respond under different circumstances.

It hardly seems necessary to say, in conclusion, that the answer to the question, "What is the minimal amount of light that can be perceived?" is not a simple one. It clearly depends both on a number of stimulus variables and on a variety of observer variables that include not only the properties of his sensory system but even those of his motivational and decision-making processes.

BIBLIOGRAPHY

ASHER, H. *Experiments in Seeing.* New York: Basic Books, 1961.

BAUMGARDT, E., & SEGAL, J. La fonction inhibitrice dans le processus visuel. *C. R. Soc. Biol.,* 1946, **140**, 231–233.

BAUMGARDT, E. Les théories photochimiques classiques et quantiques de la vision et l'inhibition nerveuse en vision liminaire. *Rev. d'Opt.,* 1949, **28**, 453–478, 661–690.

CRAWFORD, B. H. The scotopic visibility function. *Proc. Phys. Soc. Lond.,* 1949, **B 62**, 321–334.

CROZIER, W. J., & HOLWAY, A. H. Theory and measurement of visual mechanisms. I. A visual discriminometer. II. Threshold intensity and retinal position. *J. gen. Physiol.,* 1939, **22**, 341–364.

DARTNALL, H. J. A. *The Visual Pigments.* London: Methuen, 1957.

GUILFORD, J. P. *Psychometric Methods.* (2nd ed.) New York: McGraw-Hill, 1954.

HECHT, S., HAIG, C., & WALD, G. The dark adaptation of retinal fields of different size and location. *J. gen. Physiol.,* 1935, **19**, 321–327.

HECHT, S., SHLAER, S., & PIRENNE, M. H. Energy, quanta, and vision. *J. gen. Physiol.,* 1942, **25**, 819–840.

HELMHOLTZ, H. V. *Physiological Optics.* (3rd ed.) (English Translation, J. P. C. Southall) Vol. II. New York: Optical Society of America, 1924. Pp. 12–13.

HERING, E. *Outlines of a Theory of the Light Sense.* (English Translation, L. M. Hurvich and D. Jameson) Cambridge, Mass.: Harvard, 1964. P. 31 ff.

HURVICH, L. M. & JAMESON, D. Spectral sensitivity of the fovea. I. Neutral adaptation. *J. opt. Soc. Amer.,* 1953, **43**, 485–494.

LEGRAND, Y. *Light, Colour and Vision.* (English Translation, R. W. G. Hunt, J. W. Walsh and F. R. W. Hunt) London: Chapman and Hall, Chap. X.

LUCE, R. D. Detection and recognition. In *Handbook of Mathematical Psychology* (R. D. Luce, R. R. Bush, and E. Galanter, Eds.). Vol. I. New York: Wiley, 1963. Chap. III.

LYTHGOE, R. J., & PHILLIPS, L. R. Binocular summation during dark adaptation. *J. Physiol.,* 1938, **91**, 427–436.

PIÉRON, H. De la variation de l'énergie liminaire en fonction de la durée d'excitation pour la vision périphérique. *C. R. Acad. Sci.,* Paris, 1920, **170**, 1203–1206.

PIRENNE, M. H. *Vision and the Eye.* London: Chapman and Hall, 1948.

PIRENNE, M. H., & MARRIOTT, F. H. C. The quantum theory of light and the psychophysiology of vision. In *Psychology: A Study of a Science* (S. Koch, Ed.). Vol. I. New York: McGraw-Hill, 1959. Pp. 288–361.

STILES, W. S. Increment thresholds and the mechanisms of colour vision. *Documenta Ophthalmologica,* 1949, **3**, 138–165.

WALD, G. Human vision and the spectrum. *Science,* 1945, **101**, 653–658.

III

Sensitivity
to Brightness Differences

When we measure the absolute light threshold, the detection of the first brightness step occurs against a background of retinal self-light. Consequently many investigators argue that even absolute threshold determinations are based on the detection of brightness differences. This is largely a matter of definition. It is true, however, that in most of our everyday activities we are concerned with distinguishing among objects of different brightness in widely different natural and artificial illuminations.

Specific examples seem superfluous. We need only catalogue our daily activities, whatever they may be, to see that this is true. We live, work, and move about in a world where the natural illumination varies from daylight to darkness, and most of us have a variety of artificial light sources available when necessary. And in our daily environments the objects that we discriminate differ in reflectivity from almost none at all to nearly 100 percent. Since a student's life is presumably dominated by reading and studying printed material, let us therefore consider reading black print on a white background to point up some of the phenomena of brightness discrimination.

VARIABLES THAT INFLUENCE
BRIGHTNESS DISCRIMINATION

Reflectivity Differences

Needless to say, the greater the brightness difference between type and background the easier the task. As soon as our typewriter ribbon wears out and starts printing "gray" letters on white, we try to remember to change it. For a fixed level of illumination it seems obvious that two test objects with a greater difference in reflectivity between them will be more easily discriminated than a pair of objects with a smaller reflectivity difference. But the differences in perceived brightness among such objects depend importantly on the illumination level itself.

Illumination Level

If we have been working at a desk or reading in a chair during the daylight hours, as twilight approaches we find it increasingly difficult to see the printed or written material, and finally, a point is reached where an incandescent or fluorescent desk or room lamp has to be turned on if we are to continue to see our work or the black letters on the white page. Almost everyone believes that we see things better again because when we flicked on the light switch we made everything brighter. This is a very common assumption but nothing could be further from the truth. What usually happens in such circumstances is that the *brightness difference* between the black letters and the white background which has slowly been decreasing is suddenly and strongly magnified.

We have already made this point in our discussion of the uniformity of the visual world upon awakening in the middle of the night in a dark room. Under such circumstances, to try to read a book that we had left on a night table beside the bed would be absurd. What we do, of course, is to turn on a light or, if it is near morning, wait for the break of dawn when the brightness difference between the white background and the black letters starts to become magnified. Only then does the reading material become legible.

The perception of lightness differences between objects of fixed reflectivity depends critically on the level of the illumination, as this example demonstrates. Careful experiments show that as the illumination is increased from a minimal level, there is an increase in the perceived difference, but beyond some high illumination, there is a limit to the improvement. The point that needs emphasis is that although more light is reflected from *all surfaces* as the light intensity is increased the perceived brightness *difference* is increased (see Chapter VI). How this comes about varies. Depending on the circumstances, either the whites may become whiter or the blacks blacker, both the whites and blacks may change in the same direction but not to the same extent, or the one may become brighter and the other darker.

Given objects of fixed but very different reflectances, by proper manipulation of the level of illumination we can make them appear to differ considerably in brightness, or we can reduce their apparent brightness difference to zero. Still another way we can cause the apparent brightness differences to change is by manipulating the observer's adaptation level.

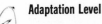

Adaptation Level

If a person has been in a brightly illuminated room and the illumination is suddenly and sharply reduced, at first nothing at all is seen or discriminated. Very shortly thereafter discrimination begins to improve, at first quickly and then more slowly until a maximum for that illumination is reached. If the illumination is now suddenly increased again, there is again an initial deterioration in the person's ability to discriminate brightness differences since he is momentarily dazzled by the bright illumination. This is soon followed by a gradual recovery and he begins once more to see differences among the various objects in the visual field.

Interaction Between Level of Illumination and Adaptation Level

In discussing the Purkinje shift and absolute thresholds, we emphasized that stimulus intensity and state of adaptation should be treated as two independent variables and not confounded. This is also true in the present situation; intensity and adaptation are independently variable, and for each adaptive state there is an illumination or intensity level at which sensitivity to differences is maximal. Furthermore, there is only one combination of adaptation and illumination level that gives optimal sensitivity, and this combination tends to differ somewhat from one individual to another. Despite the recommendations of illuminating engineers for ever more powerful lighting installations to improve ease of visual discrimination, it simply is not true that all individuals will perform best at any one standard level of illumination.

BRIGHTNESS DIFFERENCE THRESHOLDS

Luminance and Brightness Difference Threshold

What about threshold differences in brightness? How large a difference in luminance do we have to have in order to detect a minimal brightness difference between two test fields or objects? Our discussion of the absolute light threshold has made it clear that a large number of variables affect the threshold measure. Not surprisingly, the same variables influence the measure of the light difference threshold—retinal location, stimulus area, wavelength of light, adaptive state, the observer's set or expectation, and his motivational state. But if we are concerned with brightness difference thresholds, the luminance level at which we make our discrimination—that is, the level from which we measure the threshold difference—becomes the primary variable.

Persons interested in the way differential sensitivity to brightness depends on these many variables represent a variety of fields. In addition to the psychophysicist, we can list photometrists, astronomers, artists, X-ray diagnosticians, television engineers, meteorologists, microscopists, geologists, photographic film manufacturers, photographers, radar manufacturers, and aviation traffic control engineers.

In experiments to determine the least-perceptible difference in luminance, a bipartite field is typically used, with independent control of the luminance level in each half-field, and the basic judgment is a decision as to whether the two half-fields are identical in brightness or whether one is perceptibly brighter than the other. The experimental procedures appropriate for such determinations are essentially the same as those we have already discussed for the absolute threshold experiments, and all of the same precautions and controls must be exercised in order to obtain reliable and reproducible data for any given set of stimulus and observational conditions. The experiment is started with both sides of the bipartite field at the same luminance, L_1, and repeated exposures are made with each of a series of slightly higher luminances in one half-field. The observer's responses are recorded, and the luminance, L_2, is determined which he reports as brighter in 50 percent of the trials. The threshold luminance difference or increment is then

$$L_2 - L_1 = \triangle L. \tag{1}$$

Weber's Law

The major finding of first importance in such experiments is that the value of $\triangle L$ is not constant but varies systematically with the level of L_1. As the level of L_1 is increased, the difference between L_1 and L_2 must be increased in order for an observer to perceive a just-noticeable increment in brightness. If the $\triangle L$ must be increased in direct proportion to the increase in L_1, then the experimental measures would plot along a straight line of the sort illustrated in Fig. 3A. The coordinate axes in this illustrative figure are plotted in logarithmic units, which is customary in order more easily to represent the data for a wide range of stimulus luminance values. For this illustrative figure,

$$\log \triangle L = \log L + C, \tag{2}$$

or,

$$\triangle L = kL. \tag{3}$$

This relation is known as Weber's law, and is named after E. H. Weber who, in the 1830's, reported that difference limens varied in this manner

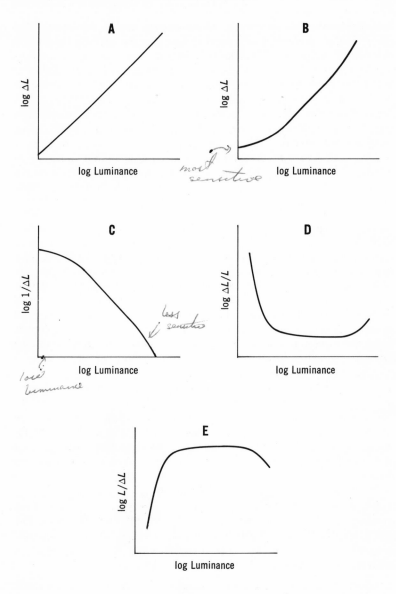

Figure 3. Relations between stimulus luminance and perception of brightness differences.

47

in judging lifted weights, pressure experiences, and visual extents. The curve in Fig. 3B more closely approximates the data actually obtained in brightness difference threshold experiments. The ΔL values increase rather slowly with L at first and then tend to approximate a straight line of direct proportionality until the very highest luminance levels are reached where the ΔL begins to increase still more rapidly than at the the intermediate luminance levels. If the stimulus value required for a threshold is increased, then we say that the observer is less sensitive, and to show this variation in sensitivity we plot the function in the form of the reciprocal ($1/\Delta L$). We remember that the luminosity function, or the relative spectral visibility function, was plotted in this reciprocal form ($1/E$) for the absolute threshold measures for lights of different wavelengths.

Brightness Difference Sensitivity

Fig. 3C thus represents the way the observer's sensitivity to luminance differences varies with increase in luminance, and we see that this difference sensitivity is high at the low luminances and drops rapidly as the luminance increases. This is not surprising: the candle flame that is so effective for after-dark dining would be wasted on a sundeck at midday. But how does this sensitivity variation jibe with our equally valid observation that we see brightness differences among objects better in high than in dim illumination? Let us take a closer look at the stimulus situations in the different instances.

Suppose the candle flame has a luminance of 1 candle/in². We can also express this in millilamberts (by referring to Table 2, Chapter I), and the value is 486 mL. Suppose further that the candle is at such a distance from the wall against which it is seen that the luminance of the candlelighted background is 1 mL. The two light fluxes add, and the total luminance of candle plus background is thus 487 mL, and the luminance difference is 486 mL. The same candle on the sun deck is seen against a sky background whose luminance is, say, 5000 mL. The total luminance of candle plus background is now 5486 mL, and the luminance difference is again 486 mL. The luminance difference is thus constant, but if we compare the two different levels of background illumination, our threshold brightness difference sensitivity may have dropped by as much as 1500-fold (Curve C, Fig. 3).

Relative Discriminability

On the other hand, if we consider the stimulus change for two objects or surfaces of different reflectance, the outcome is quite different. Suppose the two objects to be discriminated reflect 40 and 60 percent of the incident light, respectively. Let us say that the darker one has a luminance of 1 mL in candlelight; the higher luminance is then 1.5 mL. The luminance difference in candlelight is thus 0.5 mL. The same objects in sunlight might have luminances as high as 2000 and 3000 mL, respectively. The luminance difference is now 1000 mL in contrast to 0.5 mL for the same objects in candlelight, a 2000-fold increase. Thus the increase in luminance difference available for the discrimination is even greater than the maximal drop in sensitivity that is likely to occur under the two conditions of illumination, and consequently the discrimination becomes easier. In the situation in which the discrimination concerns a self-luminous source seen against a background of increasing luminance, the luminance difference is constant, and hence the experimental measure of relevance is the sensitivity measure $(1/\triangle L)$ for luminance differences. In the situation where the discrimination concerns two surfaces of different reflectance, the luminance difference grows in direct proportion to the increase in illumination, and it is the ratio of the luminance difference to the background luminance that remains constant. The threshold measure that is more directly relevant to the latter situation is a relative one, $\triangle L/L$, and the way this measure varies with luminance is shown in curve D in Fig. 3. In this plot, as the ratio, $\triangle L/L$, decreases, relative discriminability improves, and if we wish to express this relative discriminability function directly, we plot the reciprocal, $L/\triangle L$, as shown in Fig. 3E. Here we see that relative discriminability improves with increase in illumination at low levels, becomes fairly constant at intermediate levels, and drops off again at the very highest luminance values. Whether we express the data of a brightness difference threshold experiment in terms of sensitivity, Curve C, or relative discriminability, Curve E, depends on the particular problem at issue or the particular stimulus situation to which we may wish to relate the findings.

Relevant Variables Such As Luminance, Retinal Region, Exposure Time, Wavelength

Brightness difference thresholds have been measured for a variety of experimental conditions. For a fixed luminance level, the $\triangle L$ decreases as the stimulus area increases; relative discriminability, $L/\triangle L$, increases rapidly at first and then more slowly as small stimulus fields are increased in size. For test fields of fixed size and constant luminance, relative discriminability is best in the fovea and becomes poorer as the test fields are displaced to the parafovea (regions next to the fovea) and the more peripheral parts of the retina. This variation is related mainly to the fact that in the retina rods begin to replace cones as we move toward the periphery, and the neural networks in the nonfoveal regions of the retina tend to overlap more and more. But in any event, the boundaries of the test stimuli are not seen as sharply in the periphery as they are in the fovea, and it has been demonstrated that even in the fovea, the region of clearest vision, we can decrease an observer's relative discriminability simply by optically blurring the edges that separate the test fields. Other experimental data show that relative discriminability is optimal for a small separation of the two test fields and that separations greater or smaller than this critical distance cause poorer performance.

Within the limits of Bloch's law—where the product of time and intensity is constant—as we increase the stimulus duration the $\triangle L$ decreases; thus, at a fixed luminance level, our measure of relative discriminability, $L/\triangle L$, increases with exposure duration. Once we exceed very short times and move to exposures of the stimuli as long as a second or more, however, there is a degeneration in performance. This fact is well known to experts who work with telescopes, microscopes, photometers, and so forth. If the observer continues to stare at test fields his ability to detect small differences in brightness is markedly affected. To avoid this, we must introduce periodic pauses during which we deflect our gaze or close our eyes for a few seconds. Increasing exposure time thus seems at first to improve discrimination but further increases lead to decreased performance. A more complete discussion of the way the temporal variable influences brightness perception will be given in Chapter IV.

The wavelength of the light does not affect relative discriminability very much when the discrimination is between two lights of the same wavelength. The wavelength variable takes on considerable importance, however, if the two lights are of different wavelengths, particularly if a small test field of one wavelength is superposed on a larger field of a different wavelength. But here, in the determination of the so-called increment threshold, in addition to a brightness difference, color differences enter as a major factor, and they are beyond the scope of our treatment in this book.

Relative Discriminability and Adaptation

What about the effect of surround and adaptation level on relative discriminability? Should photometric test fields, for example, be viewed in the dark in the absence of an illuminated surround field, or are we better advised to view them in the center of an illuminated surround? If we use an illuminated surround how high should its luminance level be? Similar questions arise in connection with viewing X-ray plates containing small brightness differences or, for that matter, ordinary photographs. The experimental evidence is clear cut. Relative discriminability can be measured over a range of luminance values for a given adaptation and surround field. Furthermore, if a series of different surround levels is used for a fixed range of test field luminances, a family of overlapping relative discriminability functions is generated. From such a set of functions we can determine those surround conditions which favor maximal discriminability at any given test field luminance. It is found that relative discriminability tends to be best at the test field luminance which approximates that of the surround level. For surround levels either higher or lower relative discriminability becomes poorer.

Glare

Even if the surround field is spatially separated from the test fields, brightness discrimination becomes poorer as the surround luminance increases above that of the test fields. This phenomenon is of great practical importance and is usually referred to as the problem of "glare" or "glare sources." In accordance with the experimental results for moderately illuminated test fields centered in large, intense surrounds, the higher the luminance of the spatially separate secondary sources, the greater is the decrement in performance; and not surprisingly the closer the secondary "glare" source is to the test fields, the harder it is to detect a brightness difference between them. The size of a single "glare" source and its spectral composition seem to be relatively unimportant factors, but several secondary sources placed at different positions in the field act as if their effects added.

Green eyeshades for bookkeepers have gone out of fashion along with the bookkeepers themselves, but the eyeshade was a simple and effective device to keep the glare of exposed light sources from interfering with resolving the figures and writing on the page. The green eyeshade crops up again in contemporary life in the form of tinting the upper part of automobile windshields to protect the driver from the late afternoon sun. Many of us have been in homes or museums where a picture is hung between two windows and we can only see the picture and its details by shielding our eyes from the window light glare. And who has not found on more than one occasion that the glare produced by the headlights of oncoming automobiles has cut his central vision so badly that he has driven his car to the extreme right-hand side of the road to avoid what seems like certain disaster?

Glare and Stray or Scattered Light

Why is discrimination poorer in the presence of a glare source? The interpretation most commonly offered to account for this is that the light from the secondary source is scattered in the eye and acts as a "veiling glare." We have seen that the measured $\triangle L$ value is a direct function of the luminance level (Fig. 3B). Since the scattered veiling light of the secondary source is added at the retina to the primary stimulus, L_1, a greater $\triangle L$ increment is now required for a brightness discrimination, according to this interpretation.

There is, of course, no question that the eye diffusely scatters light beyond the points on the retina where a light source is sharply imaged. This is due to several factors. It is a physical effect associated with image formation by lenses and can be particularly marked in the human eye because of the cornea, lens, and the cloudy nonhomogenous media like the aqueous and vitreous humors of the eye. Stray light is also produced simply because any part of the retina that is illuminated tends to bounce a little of this light into surround regions and because light may even pass through the white (sclera) of the eye and also illuminate the retina.

All we need to do to see stray light for ourselves in our own eyes is to take a large black cardboard, pierce it with a small hole (1 mm or so) and then hold it up toward the sky in front of a window which is entirely blocked out by the black cardboard. If the small hole is first covered by a second small black card held behind the larger screen, then when we suddenly expose the hole by removing the small card, a bright rim or ring is seen that surrounds the luminous hole. This light halo is the stray or scattered light.

There is, of course, no disputing the fact that the addition of sufficient stray light will effectively reduce relative discriminability. The analogy with veiling glare can be realized by looking at test fields through a piece of glass set at 45° to the line of sight and placed in front of the test fields or objects. A piece of white paper can be held up to the side of the clear glass and its light added by reflection from the glass to the light coming from the objects. Under these circumstances, in the presence of the reflected white film, the measured ΔL is shown to increase. Stray light probably never reaches the levels that we can add by reflecting light from a white paper, but the demonstration nevertheless does illustrate one way in which stray light can interfere with discrimination.

Glare and Contrast Darkening

We shall see in a later chapter that glare sources produce darkening effects as well as the brightening effect of their light scattering action. With extensive darkening by contrast in a given retinal area, the ability to discriminate a given small luminance difference is also seriously impaired. Both half-fields become excessively dark, and their original brightness difference becomes imperceptible. If the effect of a glare source is to make both the test and comparison fields look dark, the net result is much like reducing the test and comparison field luminance levels to the low values where, as we know from Fig. 3E, relative discriminability is poorer.

E. Hering, a famous German physiologist who worked in sensory psychology, has provided several simple demonstrations of this contrast darkening effect. In one demonstration, we take a black tube about 3 cm in diameter and 30 cm long and cover one end of it with a stiff opaque white cardboard that has a 1 cm hole in its center. The open end of the tube is placed close to the eye, and we look at an etching or ink drawing on a wall opposite the window or at book shelves that have a variety of small objects on them. The details of the drawing or of the small objects can be seen very sharply and clearly. While we continue to fixate the center of the hole, the tube is suddenly removed and the white cardboard is kept in place. What we now see at the locus of the fixated hole is a grayish-black or black spot, and neither the drawing nor the objects are any longer visible within it. Gradually some details begin to be seen within the aperture, but our discrimination never reaches its original level. It could be argued that when the tube is removed the light from the white surface produces stray light. But this should cause a brightening of the aperture field and not the darkening that we observe. Although in this demonstration the darkening effect produces poorer discrimination we shall see later that there are other instances where the same darkening mechanism acts to sharpen contours and hence helps to improve our vision.

Brightness Difference Sensitivity and Principle of Availability

Brightness difference sensitivity, as we saw from Fig. 3C, is measured as the reciprocal of the $\triangle L$ values; that is, $1/\triangle L$. Since, at a fixed luminance value, the $\triangle L$ decreases with an increase in test area, a plot of $1/\triangle L$ on the ordinate against stimulus area on the abscissa shows sensitivity to be initially low and to increase as area increases. It has been proposed that this increase in sensitivity with an increase in area reflects an increase in the number of retinal elements excited. Since brightness difference sensitivity also increases with an increase in exposure time (within the limits of the validity of Bloch's law) we can reason that essentially the same mechanism operates: a longer stimulus exposure permits a greater number of elements to be excited.

Let us turn to the luminance variable. At a low luminance level a given number of retinal receptors or elements are excited; and as the stimulus level is increased, excitation is increased and more and more elements are presumably brought into play.

But what of the $1/\triangle L$ measure as a function of luminance? We have already seen from Fig. 3C that brightness difference sensitivity decreases rather than increases with an increase in luminance. Thus, whereas in the case of the area and time variables an increase in the number of excited elements leads to an increase in brightness sensitivity, in the case of the luminance variation it leads to a decrease in brightness difference sensitivity. Since there is no gainsaying the facts, the theoretical interpretation that says sensitivity increases when total excitation increases would seem to be on the wrong track.

Can we account for the area, time, and luminance effects with a single explanatory concept consistent with all the data? The answer is "yes," and the principle has been called the availability principle.

The availability principle states that differential sensitivity to brightness ($1/\triangle L$) is correlated, not with the number of elements excited, but rather with its complement: the number of available elements that remain unexcited. Differential sensitivity is then directly determined by the excitation potentially available at any moment for the discrimination of a just-noticeable difference in subjective brightness.

Let us take a specific example to see how this works. Suppose we have a uniformly illuminated, foveally located, circular light image that subtends an angle of 1° at the eye. As the illumination is increased there is a limit to the number of cells and nerve fibers that can be excited by an image of this size. This limit, however, only partly defines the potentially available excitation. Nerve fibers fire with rapid bursts of impulses whose frequency increases with increases in stimulus energy up to a maximum for each of the fibers in the area. This maximum frequency places a further restriction upon the total excitation potentially available. If we take the product of these two limits, that is, the number of fibers and the impulse frequencies, we have a precise neurophysiological definition of what we mean by the "total excitation potentially available" under these conditions. Let us specify this product by the symbol, N_P.

Now suppose this retinal image to be monochromatically illuminated at a luminance which is above the stimulus threshold. Corresponding to this luminance there will be a neural excitation, N_E. The difference between N_P and N_E at any moment defines—that is, is equal to—the excitation that remains potentially available at that moment. This difference may be written in the form of an equation,

$$N_P - N_E = N_A, \qquad (4)$$

where N_A is the remaining potentially available excitation. Relative to N_P, N_A and N_E are complementary values.

N_P will probably fluctuate somewhat depending upon the varying condition of the organism. At any moment, however, N_P may be regarded as constant for the light-image just described. As the luminance of this image is increased, N_E will increase, and N_A will therefore decrease. The results of experiments where luminance is increased demonstrate that $1/\triangle L$ also decreases as the intensity of such an image increases. Differential sensitivity is thus seen to vary directly with N_A.

Instead of varying the luminance, let us now double the area of our circular image without displacing its center or changing its shape. If doubling the stimulated area simply included twice as many foveal cones and nerve fibers and if the nerve fibers additionally available were to have the same average frequency limits as those originally involved, then for a given level of illumination, N_P and N_E have also been *doubled* when the stimulus area is doubled. Hence, relative to the image which subtends an angle of 1°, for a 2° field

$$2N_P - 2N_E = 2N_A. \tag{5}$$

The potentially available excitation N_A has also been *doubled*, and for that reason we may expect to find that $1/\triangle L$ has also increased. In fact, the neural architecture is more complex than this and becomes increasingly so for increasingly larger areas. Nevertheless, with a sufficient increase in area, it is safe to assume that N_A would probably be increased. According to the availability principle, $1/\triangle L$ would then also be expected additionally to increase.

If both the luminance and area are fixed, then the available elements with their maximum rate of firing can yield a total potential number of impulses in a given short length of time. If the time is doubled, this total potential excitation available is obviously increased. Hence the availability principle makes the same prediction for increases in exposure duration that it does for increases in area.

The availability principle is a good one to remember, for its application is not limited to brightness discrimination. It has also been used to analyze and explain discrimination problems in other modalities such as kinesthesis, audition, and somesthesis.

Monocular versus Binocular Viewing; Fechner's Paradox

Another prediction about brightness sensitivity that would seem to follow from the availability principle is that binocular viewing should yield lower threshold measures (higher sensitivity) than monocular viewing. We have already discussed the fact that absolute threshold measures do show this kind of superiority for binocular observations, and the same is true for brightness difference thresholds. Is this improved sensitivity with two eyes related to the greater number of neural elements potentially available for excitation, or is it simply a matter of an increased statistical probability of detecting a light flash, as some investigators have believed? When the statistical probability explanation was discussed in relation to absolute threshold measures in Chapter II, we pointed out that the analysis depends on the assumption that events in the two eyes are completely independent. What is the evidence on either independence or interaction that is available from comparisons of monocular versus binocular viewing?

It is, of course, well known that the two eyes working together do cooperate to give us much improved depth perception. But this fact does not really bear directly on the brightness issue.

If we place a hand over one ear or put an earplug in it, we immediately notice that the loudness of all sounds is cut down considerably.

When we remove our hand or the earplug the loudness of the fixed tone or speech is immediately restored.

Alternately shut and open one eye, say, the right one, as you look at this book. What happens? Does the page darken and lighten as you do this? There is practically no difference; the brightness of an object seen binocularly is just about the same as its brightness when viewed monocularly. The failure of the two eyes to behave as the two ears do in fact turns out to have some advantages.

We might be able to tolerate seeing the world darken each time we blinked one eye. If, however, you look straight ahead and alternately open and shut your left and right eyes, you will immediately notice that the visual fields of the two eyes do not overlap completely: some objects seen indirectly by one eye are not visible to the other. Toward the periphery there are regions of the field on each side which stimulate only one of the two retinas. If we were to look binocularly at the center of a large white sheet, and if the excitations from the two eyes summated to evoke a greater brightness where the uniocular fields overlap, we would see a bright central area surrounded by darker lateral portions. It is not hard to imagine the difficulties such a "design" would create. But since the binocularly fused brightness impression does not differ from those areas that are stimulated uniocularly, it would seem that there is no binocular brightness summation and that the events in the two eyes may indeed be completely independent.

But let us not draw the latter conclusion until we have made a few more observations. Let us place a dark gray filter or sunglass in front of only, say, the right eye, and look binocularly at this page. We have a certain impression of brightness. Now let us close or cover the right eye which has the filter in front of it. When the light entering the right eye is occluded, the page appears to lighten! On reopening the right eye and thereby adding light, the page appears to darken! With this unequal light stimulation of the two eyes we can see immediately that the excitations are not indeed independent since the fused binocular brightness impression differs strongly from that produced by the left eye alone. In this situation we have neither independence nor summation, for the added light from the right eye produces a darkening of the field rather than an increase in brightness. This effect is known as "Fechner's paradox" since it was he who first did this sort of experiment, and he had expected that the excitations from the two eyes would summate. But if the excitations from the two eyes do interact yet do not summate, what do they do? Average, perhaps? Let us make a few simple calculations based on the assumption that the process is an averaging one and that the averaging takes place for the number of eyes that contribute to the net result.

Assume the luminance level of the white background to be such that the brightness impression is 4 units. With no filters, the value is the same for each of the two eyes. For the binocular fusion situation the average brightness is:

$$\frac{4+4}{2} = 4.$$

With a dark gray filter or sunglass before each eye the luminance level is reduced so that the two separate monocular brightnesses and the binocular average brightness values are all equal to, say, 3. We now remove the filter before one eye. With this unequal stimulation there is nonetheless a unitary fused brightness impression. Four units of brightness from one eye are added to 3 units from the other and the fused brightness equals 3.5, the average for the two eyes:

$$\frac{3+4}{2} = 3.5.$$

When we shut the eye with the filter before it, and eliminate the brightness of value 3, instead of an average 3.5 brightness level we perceive a brighter unitary field of brightness value 4:

$$\frac{4}{1} = 4.$$

We might add that the increased brightness that occurs when the eye provided with a dark filter is closed does not come about because the pupil of the open eye increases in size. The pupil does enlarge somewhat under these circumstances, but Fechner in his early experiments showed that the phenomenon did not vanish when he used a small artificial pupil placed in front of the natural pupil, and he thus ruled out variation in pupil size as the causative factor. Other studies of this effect include Aubert's early work and papers by Schrödinger and Livshitz. The latter two investigators argue that the contributions coming from the two eyes are differentially weighted in the averaging process and that the more luminous of the two fields contributes proportionately more to the fused end result.

In any event, it seems clear that binocular impressions of suprathreshold brightnesses do depend on some sort of averaging of the excitations from the two eyes, and that threshold brightness and brightness difference sensitivities are improved by making the excitable neural tissue related to both eyes available for the discrimination.

Brightness Difference Thresholds and Psychophysical Laws

In Chapter I where we were concerned with the perceptual ordering of apparent brightness we pointed out that different psychophysical relations between stimulus magnitude and apparent brightness have been derived which depend largely upon the different assumptions, methods, and procedures used to establish the brightness scales. We described a simple illustrative experiment in which a brightness scale was developed by determining successive just-discriminable-brightness steps and showed how this procedure led to the Fechnerian logarithmic relation between stimulus luminance and perceived brightness. A logarithmic relation between stimulus and response was, in fact, the first of the alternative sensory scales proposed; and measurements of differential sensitivity, particularly those of Weber, form a cornerstone in the development of sensory scales.

What happened historically was that Fechner, who was concerned with the philosophical question of the relation of body and mind, saw in Weber's discrimination measures the key to solving his problem. Since Weber had found that

$$\triangle L/L = k \tag{6}$$

for a just-noticeable step in brightness, it seemed obvious to Fechner that if this physical relation of constant percentage was related to a series of equal small brightness steps, the summation of steps on both sides of the equation would lead to the basic psychophysical relation he sought.

Thus, where Weber found that

$$\triangle L/L = k \tag{6}$$

for a just-noticeable difference in brightness, Fechner extended this to

$$dI/I = k \cdot dS \tag{7}$$

where dI and dS represent *very small* concomitant differences in stimulus intensity (I) and sensation magnitude (S), respectively, and k is a constant. He then integrated this formula mathematically, which leads ultimately to the expression

$$S = k \log I, \tag{8}$$

or, as given in Chapter I for the particular brightness luminance relation,

$$B = k \log L. \tag{9}$$

Since Fechner used Weber's experiments as the base for his derivation of the logarithmic psychophysical law, we must raise two major questions. Can the relation

$$\triangle L/L = k \tag{6}$$

validly be used to encompass the facts of brightness discrimination? Obviously not. We have seen that this relation is constant for only an intermediate portion of the total stimulus range. The second question concerns the validity of Fechner's extension of Weber's finding for just-noticeable differences to equality of sensation steps. Is the ratio

$$\triangle I/I = k \tag{10}$$

valid for equal sensation steps? Do equal relative increases in stimulation produce equal increments in sensation as Fechner's law requires? Hering has described a simple experiment with lifted weights which bears directly on this question. Suppose you hold a weight of 100 g in your left hand; it will be perceived to have a certain heaviness. And if you hold 1000 g in your right hand, it will have a much greater heaviness. Now if you add an additional 100 g to the 100 g weight, and 1000 g to the 1000 g weight, then the *relative* stimulus increase on both sides is equally large. According to Fechner, since $\triangle W/W$ is the same (1.0) in both cases, Fechner's law says that the increase in apparent heaviness must also be equally large for both hands. The added 1000 g weight on the right hand must evoke the same apparent weight increase as the added 100 g weight does on the left, and you should report that the heaviness of the load has increased equally on both sides. Is the increase the same on both sides? We leave it to the reader to check this. A comparable experiment can, of course, also be carried out with lights, using equal relative luminance increments and judgments of the supraliminal brightness differences.

The interested reader who tries the visual experiment will no doubt observe that his judgments are markedly affected by the length of time during which he continues to view the stimulus fields. The importance of viewing time in measurements of brightness sensitivity is already obvious from the facts that have been discussed in this chapter and the previous one, and the role of the temporal variable in relation to other aspects of perceived brightness will be given more extensive consideration in the following chapter.

BIBLIOGRAPHY

AUBERT, H. *Physiologie der Netzhaut*. Breslau: Morgenstern, 1865.

BLACKWELL, H. R. Contrast thresholds of the human eye. *J. opt. Soc. Amer.*, 1946, **36**, 624–643.

BOYNTON, R. M., ENOCH, J. M., & BUSH, W. R. Physical measures of stray light in excised eyes. *J. opt. Soc. Amer.*, 1954, **44**, 879–886.

COBB, P. W. The effect on foveal vision of bright surroundings. IV. *J. exper. Psychol.*, 1916, **1**, 540–566.

FLAMANT, F. Sensibilité de l'oeil regardant deux points lumineux. *C. R. Acad. Sci.*, Paris, 1950, **230**, 1977–1979.

FRY, G., & ALPERN, M. The effect of a peripheral glare source upon the apparent brightness of an object. *J. opt. Soc. Amer.*, 1953, **43**, 189–195.

GRAHAM, C. H., & KEMP, E. H. Brightness discrimination as a function of the duration of the increment in intensity. *J. gen. Physiol.*, 1938, **21**, 635–650.

HECHT, S., PESKIN, J. C., & PRATT, M. Intensity discrimination in the human eye. II. The relation between $\Delta I/I$ and intensity for different parts of the spectrum. *J. gen. Physiol.*, 1938, **22**, 7–19.

HERING, E. *Outlines of a Theory of the Light Sense.* (English Translation, L. M. Hurvich and D. Jameson) Cambridge, Mass.: Harvard, 1964.

HOLLODAY, L. The fundamentals of glare and visibility. *J. opt. Soc. Amer.*, 1926, **12**, 271–319.

HOLWAY, A. H., & PRATT, C. C. The Weber-ratio for intensitive discrimination. *J. exper. Psychol.*, 1936, **43**, 332–340.

HOLWAY, A. H., & CROZIER, W. J. Differential sensitivity for somesthetic pressure. *Psychol. Rec.*, 1937, **1**, 170–176.

HOLWAY, A. H., & HURVICH, L. M. On the discrimination of minimal differences in weight: I. A theory of differential sensitivity. *J. Psychol.*, 1937, **4**, 309–332.

HOLWAY, A. H., & HURVICH, L. M. Visual differential sensitivity and retinal area. *Amer. J. Psychol.*, 1938, **51**, 687–695.

KÖNIG, A., & BRODHUN, E. Die Helligkeitsempfindlichkeit der Netzhaut. *Sitzber. Preuss. Akad. Wissensch.*, 1888, **8** (1), 917–931.

LIVSHITZ, N. N. On the laws of binocular color mixture. *C. R. (Doklady), Acad. Sci.*, USSR, 1940, **28**, 429–432.

LOWRY, E. M. Some experiments with binocular and monocular vision. *J. opt. Soc. Amer.*, 1929, **18**, 29–40.

STILES, W. S., & CRAWFORD, B. H. The liminal brightness increment for white light for different conditions of the fovea and parafoveal retina. *Proc. roy. Soc.*, 1934, **B 116**, 55–102.

SCHOUTEN, J. F., & ORNSTEIN, L. S. Measurements on direct and indirect adaptation by means of a binocular method. *J. opt. Soc. Amer.*, 1939, **29**, 168–182.

SCHRÖDINGER, E. Das Auge und die Gesichtsempfundungen. In *Lehrb. d. Physik.* (11th ed.) (Müller-Pouillet, Ed.) Vol. II. Braunschweig: Vieweg & Sohn, 1926. Chap. II.

SCHJELDERUP, H. Über eine von Simultankontrast verschiedene Wechselwirkung an Sehfeldstellen. *Z. f. Sinnesphysiol.*, 1920, **51**, 171–213.

STEINHARDT, J. Intensity discrimination in the human eye: I. The relation of $\Delta I/I$ to intensity. *J. gen. Physiol.*, 1936, **20**, 185–209.

VOS, J. J. On mechanisms of glare. Institute for Perception RVO-TNO, Soesterberg, The Netherlands, 1962.

IV

Temporal Aspects
of Brightness Perception

DEPENDENCE ON ADAPTATION LEVEL

How is our perception of the brightness of a light affected by the length of time during which we view the light? We know, of course, that the answer to this question depends on what we had been looking at before turning on the light, which we shall call the test light. Suppose we have been sitting in darkness or semidarkness for some time and that our visual system has become adapted to the low level of room illumination. Under these circumstances, if we turn on a test light of moderate luminance we find that it looks bright at first, but that it gradually loses some of its glaring quality, and finally looks relatively dim compared to its appearance at onset. On the other hand, had we come into the experimental room from outdoors on a sunny day, or had we been looking at some very strongly illuminated field for some time prior to our experiment, then the same test light would look very dim at first. As we continued to view it, however, and our eyes and visual system readjusted to the reduced amount of stimulation, the same test light would gradually increase in apparent brightness. But what if prior to the experiment, we had been exposed to a light field of precisely the same luminance as the experimental test light itself? How would the brightness of the test light vary with continued viewing time for this third condition? If our visual system had already adapted to this degree of light stimulation, that is, if it had already reached a state of equilibrium with respect to this amount of illumination of our retina, then it is clear that exposure to the test light really introduces no change in the visual response since there is no change in the visual stimulation. If the illumination to which we have previously been exposed has already achieved a steady apparent brightness, then a test light of that same luminance will also have that same apparent brightness, and it will continue to have the same appearance as long as we continue the experiment without changing the stimulus conditions. We assume that in these experiments the normal effects of eye movements are occurring and that we have done nothing to eliminate or compensate for the small tremors, flicks, or saccadic movements (rapid jumps) which our eyes show in normal use.

Having asked how the brightness of a test light varies in time as we continue to view it, we must conclude that there is no single answer. All possibilities exist. Depending on the state of adaptation of our visual system when the test light is first exposed, it may become brighter as we continue to view it, it may become darker as we continue to view it, or it may maintain a steady brightness which remains unchanged with continued viewing time. All this may seem obvious particularly when stated in the way that we have just put it, but neglect of the obvious can and sometimes does occur. An experimenter consequently must be very careful to attend to all the conditions of an experiment that might influence the state of the visual system when observations are being made.

Experimental Method

We know that the change in appearance of a light stimulus which is itself constant is caused by a change in the state of the visual system brought about by the continued action of that constant stimulus. Suppose that we wanted to obtain some quantitative measure of the amount of the time-dependent brightness changes that occur during continued viewing. We could obtain quantitative brightness estimates by one of the scaling procedures described in Chapter I. Can we devise other measures that do not depend on the various assumptions involved in scaling? One technique that can be used is a matching procedure in which we allow the test light to continue to act steadily on the eye and periodically expose a separate, comparison light which can be varied in luminance to produce the same brightness impression as our test light at successive moments in time. If the test light is becoming less bright or dimmer as we continue to view it, then to obtain a match we shall have to decrease the luminance of our variable comparison stimulus as it is exposed briefly from one time to the next. If the test stimulus is becoming brighter in appearance then we must increase the luminance of our periodically viewed comparison stimulus in order to produce an equivalent brightness impression as the test stimulus exposure continues. If the test stimulus remains constant in apparent brightness, then this fact will also be reflected by constant values for the successive matches made by adjusting the luminance of the comparison stimulus. The trick, of course, is to guarantee that the nature of our measuring rod itself, which is the reaction to each level of the comparison light, remains unchanged from one moment to the next if our variable comparison stimulus measures are to have any meaning.

We can come closest to guaranteeing this constancy of the measuring instrument by exploiting the fact that the observer has two separate eyes and that, if we arrange the optical stimulus conditions correctly, he can make comparisons between the perceptions produced by the continuously viewed test stimulus in one eye and those produced by the brief comparison stimuli in the other eye. If the stimulating conditions for the comparison, or measuring, eye are kept constant for a sufficiently long time before the beginning of the experiment and between experimental measures, then this eye will be in an approximately steady equilibrium condition throughout the experiment. The exposures of the comparison stimuli to the measuring eye must, of course, be rather brief in order not to disturb its equilibrium condition excessively, and the time that elapses between successive exposures of the comparison stimulus must be long enough so that whatever disturbances in equilibrium do occur will be overcome and the steady state reestablished before the next brightness matching judgment is made.

How do we compare the separate impressions from the two eyes? Normally when both eyes are open and we are using binocular vision we are not aware of the separate impressions from our left and right eyes. But if you were to stand a piece of cardboard on the page you are now reading so as to divide the page into a left and a right half, and if you positioned your head so that the middle of your forehead and the tip of your nose were aligned with the cardboard, then you would be able to read the left half of the page only with your left eye and the right half only with your right eye. This is the essence of the experimental situation in which, typically, we set up two semicircular fields and allow the left and right halves to be seen, respectively, by the left and right eyes. When the physical separation of the two semicircles is properly adjusted for the viewing distance and the particular observer, then, with both eyes open, a full circular field with a vertical dividing line through the center is seen. If we now illuminate, say, the right half of our bipartite circular field with the steady test light and present the variable comparison light periodically in the left half of the field that is seen only by the left eye, then we have the necessary optical conditions for making brightness comparisons and matches. This kind of experimental arrangement artificially separates the visual system into two halves and permits separate and more or less independent manipulation of the two visual states for the two eyes. Experiments of this sort are sometimes called "binocular" matching experiments. Since the word binocular is more appropriately used to describe the ordinary situation where both eyes view the same objects, a better word to describe this particular experimental arrangement is "haploscopic."

In such a haploscopic experiment we might choose for the steady state of the measuring eye, the condition of adaptation to darkness. If, before the beginning of the experiment, the observer has remained in total darkness for 20 to 30 minutes, then both eyes will initially be in the same dark-adapted state. At the outset of the experiment, therefore, brief exposures of test lights to the right eye will presumably be matched, using equally brief exposures to the left, comparison eye, by light stimuli of the same luminance as the test stimuli. A plot of the results of such an experiment would simply show that the matching luminance of the variable comparison stimulus varies in direct proportion to the luminance of the series of test stimuli. This is, of course, a trivial result, and the only reason for doing this experiment at all is to assure the experimenter that his subject sees lights in the same way with each of his two eyes— obviously a necessary condition for doing haploscopic experiments of this sort. Once the control results have been established, we may begin to investigate the way that the brightness perceptions are altered with continued viewing time. The experiments that we shall consider first concern the differences in apparent brightness between the time of initial exposure and the time at which the continued light stimulus takes on a steady brightness. A well-known and frequently cited series of experiments was carried out by K. J. W. Craik in England in 1940. His interest was in the change between the brightness perception on initial stimulation and the brightness perception when the equilibrium state for the same amount of continued light stimulation is achieved.

DEPENDENCE ON LUMINANCE LEVEL; STEADY-STATE CONDITION

In one series of Craik's experiments, both eyes were initially dark adapted for 20 minutes, and then a very dim light stimulus was presented to the right eye. The light intensity of this stimulus was between 0.001 and 0.01 mL. The left eye remained in darkness while the dim test stimulus continued to be viewed by the right eye until its apparent brightness had reached a steady level. When the steady state was achieved, the test stimulus in the right eye was momentarily shut off, and a comparison stimulus was presented to the left eye for approximately 1 second. The observer reported whether or not the briefly exposed comparison light seen by his left eye appeared to be brighter or dimmer than the stimulus that was steadily viewed by the right. The steady test stimulus seen by the right eye was occluded only during the 1 second exposure of the comparison stimulus to the left. After each judgment the comparison luminance was adjusted and after about 5 seconds was exposed again. The procedure was repeated in a series of bracketing steps until the experimenter had determined the approximate value of the stimulus in the left, dark-adapted eye that matched the steady brightness of the continuing test stimulus in the right eye. For the very dim initial stimulus of the series, the matching luminance for the left eye was slightly lower than the luminance value of the steady stimulus in the right eye. For a series of steady test stimuli at increasing luminance levels, it was found that the matching luminance had to be increased but that it had to be increased at a much slower rate than the increase in the test luminance to which the right eye was exposed. Thus, unlike the control data that we just described, a plot of the results of this experiment do not show the matching luminance to increase in direct proportion to the luminance of the test stimulus. Rather, Craik found that the matching luminance varies approximately in proportion to the square root of the test luminance from the minimal value up to approximately 100 mL. Between 100 and 1000 mL, the matching values continue to increase but at a still slower rate, and beyond 1000 mL, all of the test stimuli at the increasing levels of luminance to which the right eye has become adapted appear to have the same steady brightness. All stimuli above 1000 mL are matched by a single constant value of the briefly exposed comparison stimulus in the dark-adapted left eye. It should be noted that as the luminance of the test stimuli is increased, and the luminance of the brief flashes presented to the dark-adapted left eye is also increased somewhat, the time allowed for recovery of the dark-adapted condition must be increased from the initial 5 second recovery interval for the lowest stimulus levels to approximately 1 minute for the highest values.

Some notion of the extent to which the continued exposure of a steady stimulus can reduce its apparent brightness as compared with its initial appearance to the maximally light sensitive, dark-adapted eye, can be gained from Craik's quantitative finding that the steady brightness produced by all of the test stimuli from about 1000 to 15,000 mL is the same as the brightness produced by a stimulus whose luminance is only 3 mL when it is seen for only one second by a dark-adapted eye.

As is true of all numerical values for the results of visual experiments, these particular luminance values are valid only for the specific conditions of Craik's experiments. Changes in the size of the test stimulus, for example, or in the exposure durations of the brief comparison stimuli, will alter the specific values obtained in any given experiment.

Experiments of the sort reported by Craik give us a measure, in terms of units of the matching stimulus, of the difference in the appearance of a light from the moment that it is first seen with the dark-adapted eye to the time when it has been viewed long enough to achieve a steady brightness. Craik's study also includes other series of experiments in which the left eye, which briefly viewed the matching stimuli, was adapted to various levels of luminance in addition to the dark-adapted condition. The maintenance of the dark-adapted state for the comparison is, however, more typical of many studies of this general sort that have been reported in the literature.

BRIGHTNESS CHANGES BEFORE STEADY STATE IS REACHED

Experimenters have also been interested in following the changes in appearance of a test stimulus during the time in which the eye is becoming adapted to it and before the steady, equilibrium state is reached. Typically, it is found that the apparent brightness of a continuously exposed test light decreases rather rapidly during the first few seconds and that the changes required in the matching stimulus after a minute or so are relatively small as the steady state brightness of the test stimulus is approached.

Paradoxical Finding

One series of experiments concerned with the time course of the brightness changes of continuously viewed colored stimuli yielded a conflicting result. Instead of a decrease in apparent brightness with continued exposure, it was reported that the apparent brightness of a test stimulus increased with continued exposure. This seemingly paradoxical result, which was reported in 1946, was assumed to have something to do with the fact that the stimuli were colored, and rather complicated speculations about interactions between brightness and hue mechanisms were put forth to account for it.

Adaptation Level Factor

But the reason for the result is actually rather simple and obvious and has nothing to do with hue. We have already emphasized that the way the apparent brightness of a light changes with continued exposure depends strongly on the state of the visual system when the test light is first exposed. To demonstrate that the seemingly paradoxical brightness result is really a predictable, and not at all paradoxical, outcome of the specific experimental conditions, consider the following experiment that we reported in 1949. Colored test stimuli of relatively low luminances, of the sort used in the original study, were employed as the test lights, and three different series of haploscopic matching experiments were conducted with the same test lights. In the first series, the two eyes were initially exposed for some time to identical gray fields whose luminance level was considerably less than that of the chromatic test stimuli. After these preexposure fields had achieved a steady brightness for both eyes, the colored test stimulus was exposed to the right eye, and the left eye continued to view the neutral preexposure field. Short exposures of comparison stimuli were made in the left eye, and the luminances of these briefly exposed comparison stimuli were varied to match the apparent brightness of the continued colored stimulus in the right eye at various moments in time after the onset of the test field. In comparison to the steady brightness of the preexposure stimulus, each test light at first appeared quite bright, and in time with continued viewing, its apparent brightness decreased, rather rapidly at first and later more slowly until the steady brightness was achieved. This, of course, is the typical finding in such experiments, and it is not surprising to obtain it again here since the low luminance level of the preexposure fields does not differ greatly from the dark preexposure condition that we said earlier is most frequently used as a standard initial state.

In the second experimental series, the level of the neutral preexposure fields was increased to a luminance that was identical to the luminance of the colored test stimuli. Now it was found that the test stimulus had the same apparent brightness as the neutral preexposure field when it was first viewed, and it continued to maintain this same steady brightness throughout the exposure duration, which continued for some minutes. If we had only this second result, we might conclude that apparent brightness is constant and independent of exposure duration, a conclusion very different from the typical finding.

In the third series of experiments, the initial luminance of the preexposure fields was somewhat higher than that of the chromatic test stimuli. For this condition, the right eye that had reached an equilibrium level after viewing the preexposure field saw the test stimulus of lower luminance as quite dim when it was first exposed, and with continued exposure, as the state of the visual system readjusted toward a new equilibrium condition with respect to the continued test stimulation, the apparent brightness of the test stimulus gradually increased and finally reached a steady value which was higher than the initial level. Once again, the result is not a surprising one when we take into account the state of the system when the test light is first exposed, nor is it surprising to find that this third series of experiments duplicates the preexposure and test stimulus levels used in the original experiment that yielded the "paradoxical" increase in brightness with continued light exposure.

What we must remember in any visual experiments, and in the description of any visual phenomenon, is that we are always observing the reactions of our visual system to *changes* in stimulation and not simply to a given test stimulus. If the change in stimulation is in the direction of a lower stimulus level, then our perceptions will vary in time in one way; if the change is in the direction of a higher level of stimulation, our perceptions will vary in time in an opposite way; and if the level of stimulation does not actually represent a change, and we have already allowed the system to come to equilibrium with the preexisting level, then we may expect to find that our brightness perception continues to maintain the same steady level.

We should emphasize again that the specific dependence of apparent brightness on viewing time, its rate of change and the steady level that it finally reaches, vary with all the stimulating conditions, such as the size of the test field, retinal location, and so on.

FIXED RETINAL IMAGES

Steady Fixation

In the haploscopic experiments we have been discussing, the viewing situation is not a normal one in that the impressions from the two eyes are artificially separated, and the highly controlled stimulus conditions differ for the two eyes. Nevertheless, the situation does involve normal eye movements. What happens if we try to fixate continuously and very steadily so that eye movements are reduced to a minimum? Suppose you make a small pencil mark in the center of a sheet of white paper, fixate it steadily, and then hold the pencil in a fixed position above and near the edge of the paper so that it casts a dim shadow on the white paper while you continue to look as steadily as possible at your fixation mark. Suppose further, that before the shadow is cast, you have been looking at the paper long enough so that it has reached a steady apparent brightness. Now when the shadow is first cast it will appear as a relatively dark area on the paper in the periphery of your field of view. The luminance of the shadow stimulus is, of course, lower than the unshadowed luminance of the white paper. Since this is true we know from the experiments that we have been discussing above that, in time, this shadow area will increase somewhat in apparent brightness as contrasted to its brightness on initial appearance. What will the steady brightness of the shadow area become?

If you do this demonstration experiment carefully and if you are able to fixate very steadily, you will find that in time the shadow initially seen in the periphery of your field of view eventually disappears completely: the shadow area finally reaches the same apparent brightness as the remainder of the field of view provided by the white paper. As soon as you shift your fixation away from the pencil mark, however, the shadow will reappear. This is very simply because when your eyes move, the lower luminance of the shadow area now represents a change in stimulation for the part of your retina that had just been in equilibrium with respect to the level of stimulation from the white paper surround, and consequently the change in stimulation is again registered as a change in the brightness response. If you were to hold your eyes steadily in the new fixation direction established by moving the eyes away from the original fixation point, then the same gradual disappearance of the shadow would be repeated once more. Except when we are staring vacantly into space and not really "looking" at anything, this sort of fading of external objects or differently illuminated areas does not normally occur. In everyday viewing, our eyes are constantly in motion, and we are continuously shifting our fixation from one part of the field of view to another. Our retinas are therefore constantly subjected to *changes* in stimulation. As we have seen from the shadow demonstration, the existence of eye movements is a necessary functional part of our visual mechanism, and without them our visual perceptions would obviously soon lose any useful function for commerce with the world of objects about us.

Anatomical Shadow-Casters

On the other hand, in our eyes, anatomical structures are present between light incident at the cornea and light reaching the sensitive layers of the retina. These structures are, so to speak, permanent shadow-casters, and they include the variable thickness of macular pigment that surrounds the fovea and the network of retinal blood vessels. We are ordinarily not aware of them at all because, like the pencil shadow when our fixation was steadily maintained, their retinal shadows are constant and our eyes are completely adapted to them. Only early in the morning when we are adapted to darkness can we sometimes get a glimpse of the macular pigment shadow when the room is first illuminated, or else by special techniques of changing illumination or strong illumination directed from the side through the semiopaque wall of the eyeball can we reveal the so-called entoptic phenomena produced by these built-in, stationary shadow-casters in the eye. Fortunately, these shadows do not vary in position with eye movements, and consequently they do not interfere with our useful visual perceptions.

Ganzfeld

We may emphasize the functional necessity of normal eye movements by citing a further class of experiments. In order to produce a visual stimulus field that would remain unchanged on the retina in spite of the continuous motion of the eye, Hochberg, Triebel, and Seaman used the following procedure. In front of each eye with the lids open, they placed one half of a ping-pong ball that formed a diffuse, translucent hemisphere around the outer part of the eyeball. They then illuminated each hemisphere uniformly by shining an external light source on it, and the observer consequently had his whole retina uniformly illuminated by the light coming through the hemisphere. The homogeneous field is commonly called *Ganzfeld*, the German word for "total field." Since the ping-pong ball itself was uniformly illuminated, movements of the eye behind it produced no change whatsoever in the stimulation of any part of the retina. Under these circumstances, when the light was turned on the subject initially saw a uniformly colored field of some brightness, and as the duration of exposure to the same unchanged retinal stimulation continued, the total field gradually decreased in apparent brightness, and finally after some time, the subject no longer perceived any light stimulation at all. Some of them suspected that the experimenter had gradually turned the stimulus light off. The effect of continued, really unchanging stimulation on the retina therefore becomes equivalent, in terms of useful visual perceptions, to having no stimulation at all. Now, in order to reactivate the visual system, the experimenter could either increase or decrease the light on the ping-pong ball, cast a shadow or a small intense spot of light on it, and once again the observer was able to see something as a result of the *change* in visual stimulation. This must be emphasized, because the reason for the stimulus disappearance in these experiments is not that the visual system has become so insensitive that the stimulus level has to be increased in order to produce an effect; any *change* will be effective whether it be an increase or a decrease in the level of stimulation.

A procedure known as the Hering dimming technique demonstrates the same point. If we look continuously at a small disk of light in an otherwise dark room and fixate it rigorously, the brightness of the disk gradually decreases for about 20 to 30 seconds and the overall field becomes uniformly dark. If the disk illumination is now suddenly decreased, or better still, cut off completely for a brief moment or so, we see a disk which is blacker than the overall uniform darkness of the room.

ACTION-REACTION DUAL PROCESS

All of these experiments illustrate a very important property of the way the visual mechanism responds to light. The behavior of the visual system clearly must be conceived as having not one, but two, basic response characteristics. One is the *action* produced by a light stimulus on the visual apparatus. The other is the *reaction* process. The action process set off by a light stimulus seems itself to give rise to a reaction process, a response that is in some sense opposite to the action response. The concept is illustrated in an oversimplified, schematic fashion in Fig. 4. The horizonal dimension of the diagram represents a variation in time

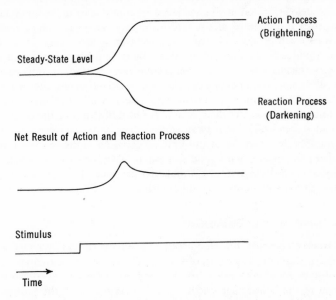

Figure 4. Temporal course of action (brightening) and reaction (darkening) processes.

from left to right. At some point in time on the extreme left of the temporal dimension, we may assume that the visual system has been protected from external stimulation for some time, and that the ongoing action and reaction processes are in balance. In the absence of external stimulation, these processes are presumably initiated by fluctuations in the internal condition of the living organism. The action response to a light stimulus of a system in this state rises at first, and, as we have shown, it reaches a plateau at the end of some period of time during which the stimulation continues unchanged. As the action process begins, it constitutes a change in the state of the visual tissue, and this change gives rise to the reaction process, which we have diagrammed as increasing in the opposite direction. The reaction process shows a drop from the base line, and it too is shown as reaching a steady level after some time. The brightness impression may be thought of as the resultant of these two opposite effects. When the action process caused by a stimulus has continued for a sufficiently long time so that the reaction process, which is opposite to it, has become equal to it in magnitude, then as far as the brightness of the perception is concerned, the resultant of these two equal and opposite effects will be a total cancellation, and will be equivalent, in brightness terms, to the absence of stimulation. If the stimulus field is limited in size and the eyes continue to move while viewing it, then this state of affairs will ordinarily not occur, since the eye movements will produce changes in stimulation at least at the boundaries of the stimulus fields. Particularly if the light field has sharply delimited contours, the changes in stimulation around these contours produced even by small tremor movements will be abrupt, relatively large, and definitely significant. Our peripheral shadow experiment is effective only because the luminance across the shadow area is not uniform, but the density of the shadow gradually fades away at the edges, as we move from umbra to penumbra. It is because of this gradual variation in the shadow brightness that it is possible, with good fixation, to have the shadow completely disappear since the changes in stimulation produced by small eye movements are themselves only very slight changes.

Optical Devices for Image Stabilization

Other techniques for eliminating the effects of eye movements in producing shifts of the pattern of stimulation on the retina involve special optical devices. These devices are designed in such a way as to cause the location of the light image on the retina to depend upon the position of the eye itself. One such technique involves the use of a contact lens on the eye with a mirror attachment which is used to alter the direction of the stimulus light path as the eye is moved. Since the alterations in the direction of the incident light are almost perfectly correlated with the eye movements by such a contact lens and mirror device, the image continues to fall on precisely the same part of the retina as the eyeball moves from one position or orientation to the next. A related technique involves placing a small stalk on a contact lens, with a miniature stimulus and imaging device located at the end of the stalk. Again when the eye moves and the contact lens with it, so does the stalk and the image forming device, and thus the image remains painted, as it were, on the retina even though the eyes are able to continue in constant motion. In all of these instances the perceptions after continued viewing are the same as those we have already described for the homogeneous *Ganzfeld*. With continued exposure to light stimulation that falls on the same part of the retina in an unchanging way, in time a complete equilibrium state is reached—there is no differential brightness perception and no perception of an image delineated by contours of different brightness. These ingenious optical means for eliminating changes in retinal stimulation caused by eye movements have been devised, respectively, by Riggs and his co-workers in the United States, and by Ditchburn and his co-workers in England. The techniques have been applied to the study of a variety of specific theoretical issues, and the main effects of stimulus washout or perceptual fading are cited here as further evidence for the general schema shown in our illustrative diagram. The two opposite processes of action and reaction that occur as a result of visual stimulation are clearly demonstrated when any of these special techniques are used to maintain the local stimulation of the retina constant in time which allows these two opposite processes to reach equal magnitude and thus cancel their relative contributions to apparent brightness.

Afterimages

The action and reaction processes that appear to characterize the visual system are manifested most clearly in afterimage phenomena. Afterimage demonstrations permit us to separate, as it were, the action-reaction processes by terminating the primary stimulus abruptly. This permits the reaction process to be displayed in the absence of further external stimulation or in the presence of different "secondary" stimuli.

The many details and hundreds of experiments devoted to afterimage phenomena are not our primary concern here. What we should like to emphasize is that it is a fairly simple matter to demonstrate that after continued steady fixation for 20 to 30 seconds of a moderately bright disk on a black background we need only turn our gaze to a completely uniform white field and note there the appearance of a dark gray or black afterimage disk. The white primary image can be said to represent dominance of the action process, and the dark afterimage which replaces it the reaction process. In the same way a black disk seen against a white background produces a white afterimage in complete darkness under appropriate conditions.

Colored afterimages demonstrate the action-reaction processes even more dramatically. Red stimuli produce complementary green afterimages and vice versa; blue stimuli produce complementary yellow afterimages and vice versa. But these color phenomena are beyond the scope of this book.

All afterimages are not negative or complementary. Positive afterimages which exhibit the same relative brightnesses or the same colors as the primary stimuli can also be produced by appropriate manipulations of the experimental conditions. However, careful analyses of these conditions—that is, relative test and background luminances in the primary stimulation and background illumination of the secondary stimulation—only serve to strengthen the view that the afterimage effects are products of an action-reaction mechanism rather than the result of retinal or neural fatigue as is sometimes argued.

BRIGHTNESS CHANGES DURING VERY SHORT EXPOSURES

The temporal effects that we have been discussing are effects that occur during seconds and minutes. Our schematic illustration shows that the time course of the initial action and reaction processes that follow the stimulus onset is not infinitely fast but shows in each instance a gradual increase before it reaches the steady plateau. What happens to the apparent brightness of a light during the very early phase of the gradual change? When we ask this question, we are addressing ourselves to the effects of exposure duration, not for times of minutes or even seconds, but rather of hundredths or thousandths of a second.

Experimental Data

Among the first quantitative data that deal with the way apparent brightness varies during times of these extremely short orders of magnitude were those reported by Broca and Sulzer in France in 1902. Broca and Sulzer compared the apparent brightnesses of light stimuli that were observed for a second or more with those exposed for very short durations of 0.01 second to about 0.05 second. The comparison light that was viewed for a second or more was made variable in luminance so that it could be matched in apparent brightness to the very short pulses of the test light of fixed luminance for a series of durations of the test light pulses. The essence of their experimental procedure is approximately as follows. The longer, variable luminance comparison field is turned on, and then, next to it, the test light is flashed for a fraction of a second. The observer must judge whether one or the other of the adjacent light fields is the brighter. After each judgment, the luminance of the comparison field is adjusted to bring it nearer to the apparent brightness of the very brief test flash. In a given series of measures, the luminance of the test flash is kept at some predetermined level, and the flash duration is increased from the shortest pulse time through increasingly longer test flashes. Even though the luminance of the test flash remains fixed, the apparent brightness of the flash does indeed vary as the exposure duration is varied, and the changes in apparent brightness are evaluated by the changes in the comparison stimulus luminance required for a brightness match. The matching luminance measures are repeated for the same durations of test flash but for different test stimulus luminances. This makes it possible to describe the differences in the way the brightness sensation develops in time for test lights of different luminances. What Broca and Sulzer found was that the apparent brightness of very feebly illuminated test fields rises rather slowly to a maximum level during the first fractions of a second. The apparent brightness of very strongly illuminated test fields, however, rises very rapidly and shows a definite overshoot during the first few fractions of a second and then levels off at an apparent brightness considerably lower than the initial maximum. This means that if a test stimulus of fairly high luminance is used, it actually appears much brighter when it is exposed for, say, 0.05 second than when it is exposed for 0.5 second. This very rapid initial overshoot in the apparent brightness of light stimuli of high luminance has been confirmed and explored more fully by many other investigators, but it is commonly referred to as the Broca-Sulzer phenomenon after the French scientists who obtained and reported quantitative measures of this effect.

Explanation

How are we to account for the Broca-Sulzer phenomenon? Let us turn again to our schematic illustration for a straightforward and undoubtedly oversimplified account of this effect. If we look closely we see that the action process initiated by the light stimulus begins before the reaction process is initiated. If the action process is correlated with the perception of brightness and its opposite, the reaction, is a darkening effect, then clearly the brightening begins before the darkening comes in to counteract it. Thus there will be a very short time during which the brightness action alone is operative, and a further, still short, interval during which the opposite darkening reaction lags appreciably behind the brightness action. When the brightness action is rising steeply, the brightness perception will be increasing steeply. As soon as the opposite darkening process of reaction begins to come into play, however, the resultant of the two opposite processes will begin to diminish in amount and the brightness perception will be rapidly brought down to a lower level.

Broca and Sulzer themselves described two opposite processes of much this sort, but the concepts that they used were those of excitation and fatigue. The concept of fatigue, with all its usual connotations, does not, however, seem very appropriate to describe effects that occur in such very short fractions of a second.

In the nineteen-forties, comparable notions were developed and described in much greater detail by two other investigators also working in France, Baumgardt and Segal, who used for the two opposite visual processes the concepts of excitation and inhibition. We prefer here, however, to avoid the concept of inhibition to describe the reaction process, since inhibition implies simply a negation of positive effect, and we find more useful Hering's original idea of a reaction process that does not simply negate but that has positive blackness perceptions correlated with it.

BRIGHTNESS ENHANCEMENT

In developing their detailed theoretical ideas about the interaction of excitation and inhibition processes, Baumgardt and Segal were especially interested in providing a common explanation for the Broca-Sulzer phenomenon that we have been discussing, and for a brightness enhancement effect that occurs with flickering lights that is generally known as the Brücke-Bartley phenomenon. Before discussing the brightness enhancement phenomenon that occurs with flickering light stimuli at certain rates, it would be profitable to have an overview of the general problem of flickering stimuli in vision. We shall then be able to place the Brücke-Bartley effect in the context of the flicker problem as a whole, and also relate it both to the Broca-Sulzer overshoot in apparent brightness for very short times and to the concept of two opposite visual response processes that seems to be required by this phenomenon.

Analysis of Flicker Fusion Experiments

In the experiments that we have been discussing above, each very brief light flash was followed by a dark interval of an appreciable duration. Under these circumstances, the individual light flashes are distinctly seen as separate flashes of some brightness determined by the luminance of the stimulus and the duration of the individual test flash. What happens if we use trains of repeated light flashes separated by dark intervals of the same duration as each light flash itself? A convenient way to do this is to use a half open and half opaque sector disk mounted on the rotating shaft of a motor in front of a light source. When this sector disk revolves in front of the light source, the light source will be seen during half the time and it will be occluded during the remaining half of each full rotation by the opaque half of the disk. If the disk is rotated at a speed of, say, one full revolution per second, then a series of alternating light flashes and dark intervals will be perceived. As the speed of rotation is increased the separate flashes begin to be lost, and a flickering light field is seen. As the speed of rotation is increased still further a point will eventually be reached at which flicker is no longer perceived, and the perception becomes one of a continuous light of steady brightness. The speed of alternation at which the interrupted light stimulus changes from just perceptibly flickering to just no longer flickering can be measured quite accurately, and this rate of alternation is known as the critical flicker frequency or critical fusion frequency, commonly abbreviated cff. The frequency of light-dark alternation required for the cff may be as low as about 15 flashes per second for foveal light stimulation. The cff increases as the luminance of the test light increases up to a maximum of approximately 60 flashes per second, and beyond this speed of alternation flicker is not usually perceived. The regular way in which the critical flicker frequency rises with increase in the luminance of the stimulus is generally known as the Ferry-Porter law. This law states that cff increases in direct proportion to the logarithm of the stimulus luminance. Like most visual laws, it is only approximately true. The direct proportionality holds for an intermediate range of test luminances only. At very low levels of luminance the rate of increase in cff is somewhat slower than directly proportional to log luminance, and again at very high levels the rate decreases, and, as we have just said, it reaches a maximum at about 60 cycles per second with no further increase at still higher luminances. It is, of course, this capacity of our visual system to fuse to a steady brightness rapidly alternating light and dark intervals that enables us to employ alternating current for our electric light systems without being subjected to annoying flicker.

Let us look more closely at the way that flicker perception depends on the luminance of the repetitive light flashes. We know that a fused, continuous brightness is perceived with a relatively slow repetition rate when the stimulus luminance is at a low level, but that the flash rate must be increased considerably when the luminance level is increased. The perception of flicker, the waxing and waning of a light impression in time, can be described as the discrimination of an intensity difference in time. In Chapter III in the discussion of intensity discrimination experiments, we saw that the difference in luminance required to perceive a difference in brightness increases with the luminance of the background light stimulus. According to Weber's law, which holds for an intermediate range of stimulus intensities, the difference limen increases in nearly direct proportion to the test stimulus level. In the absence of any other information about the temporal response characteristics of the visual system, one might suppose as the simplest starting assumption that, with repetitive pulsing of alternating light-dark stimulus intervals, the effective stimulus difference between light flash and succeeding dark intervals would increase in direct proportion to the stimulus intensity. If this were an adequate and accurate analysis, then since ΔI and I are equal for all stimulus levels, one should presumably perceive flicker or perceive a steady, fused brightness at the same alternation rate for all stimulus levels. We have just said that this is not so.

But this incorrect analysis ignores relevant information about the response of the visual system to temporal variations in light stimuli. We know that for single brief light pulses at low levels of luminance, the brightness impression gradually increases as the duration of the light pulse is increased during a few fractions of a second. For stimuli of high luminances, moreover, we know that the so-called sensation rise time, or the growth of brightness impression, occurs more abruptly and at a much more rapid rate than for relatively weak light stimuli. The brightness effect of each individual light pulse in a sequence of light-dark alternations of the same duration (that is, for a single rate of alternation) is consequently disproportionately greater for the pulses of higher luminance than for those of lower luminance. In view of this dependence of brightness rise time on stimulus luminance, it is not surprising that a pulse rate that produces a fused brightness impression and that is beyond the limits of the system for the temporal resolution of a ΔI at a low level of luminance is readily resolved at a higher luminance level and that the high luminance stimulus at this rate of alternation continues to be perceived as flickering. But this temporal resolution at high stimulus levels must also mean that not only the action process of the visual system but also the reaction process must be faster when the system is stimulated more intensely. That is, the brightness impression for the higher luminances must not only rise more rapidly during the light interval, it must also decline more rapidly during the dark interval. With both processes occurring more rapidly as luminance increases, the speed of alternation must be increased to eliminate the perception of flicker. There are, of course, limits to the speed of both the action and reaction processes, and this intuitively reasonable expectation is confirmed by the fact that cff does not exceed approximately 60 cycles per second even for the highest levels of light stimulation.

Talbot's Law

We have been discussing the way the brightness of an intermittent light stimulus either fluctuates in time and is perceived as flickering or fails to show any fluctuation. What about the apparent brightness of an actually intermittent stimulus that is perceived as steady as compared with that of a stimulus that continues in time without physical interruption? For information on this question, we may set up another matching experiment in which we judge the brightness of an intermittent light stimulus pulsed at a rate well above the fusion threshold relative to that of a steady light stimulus in the other half of our matching field. On the basis of such matching experiments, it has been found that the two fields are equal in apparent brightness when the luminance of the continuous stimulus is equal to the average luminance of the intermittent stimulus that is seen as fused. If the intermittent stimulus is on for half the cycle and off for the other half, then its luminance per unit time averaged over the whole cycle will be equal to one half the luminance of the light flash itself. This average luminance value per unit time will appear to be of exactly the same brightness as a light stimulus of that same average luminance that stays on continuously. This general finding is known as Talbot's law, and it is not uncommon in the visual literature to specify the level of an intermittent stimulus by this average value and to denote it as the "Talbot luminance."

Brücke-Bartley Brightness Enhancement

An interesting brightness phenomenon occurs, however, when the speed of alternation of light and dark intervals is reduced to a rate considerably below that required for fusion. At these lower rates the intermittent light is seen as flickering, and the apparent brightness of the flickering light is considerably greater than the steady brightness seen when pulses of the same luminance are repeated at a much faster rate above the fusion level. This increased brightness of the flickering light is the Brücke-Bartley brightness enhancement effect to which we referred earlier. Bartley has made an intensive study of this brightness enhancement phenomenon, and reports that under many conditions it is maximal when the rate of alternation is approximately 10 to 12 cycles per second. He interprets the phenomenon as closely related to the alpha rhythm that can be recorded in the human electroencephalogram and which has approximately this same periodicity. Bartley has described his idea of the way the system reacts to intermittent light stimulation in terms of what he calls the "alternation of response theory." The basic idea is that all neural units react to stimulation with a burst of activity and then require an interval for recovery before they can react again. The dynamic properties of the neural units are presumably such that the activity and recovery periods can be maximally synchronized throughout all neural units at precisely that rate at which maximal brightness enhancement occurs, and it is for this reason that the alpha rhythm, which presumably reflects a synchronization of spontaneous cortical activity, shows the same rate of cycling. It should be pointed out that many investigators do not agree with Bartley on the correspondence between alpha rhythm periodicity and the flicker rate at which maximal brightness enhancement occurs. There is little, if any, disagreement, however, on the fact that under certain conditions the brightness enhancement phenomenon can be demonstrated with flickering lights. But, if we leave aside the controversial question of the relevance to the brightness effect of synchronized spontaneous cortical activity, it remains true that Bartley's alternation of response theory bears certain resemblances to the very general idea of visual response that we have been describing throughout this chapter. The notion of bursts of activity followed by recovery is certainly not unrelated to the idea of excitation and fatigue that was used by Broca and Sulzer to describe the processes underlying the brightness overshoot phenomenon for single very brief light pulses. We also mentioned earlier that Baumgardt and Segal, who described the two opposite processes involved in the brightness response as excitation and inhibition, sought to derive specific relations between the Broca-Sulzer phenomenon and the brightness enhancement effect.

Baumgardt and Segal's Hypothesis

Baumgardt and Segal's hypothesis was essentially as follows. When excitation is produced in a neural element by stimulation of the eye, a double effect occurs. First there is an increased instability in the neural element that favors further excitation, and this effect they call facilitation. Then there is a stabilization that tends to oppose itself to any new excitation, and this process they call inhibition. The temporal evolution of the excitatory, facilitating process necessarily leads that of stabilization and inhibition. Consequently, they reasoned that, after this double process has been set into action by a very brief pulse of light stimulation, a second pulse that follows very closely in time may bring about an excess of the excitatory over the inhibitory effect, and the apparent brightness of the double flash will be seen to increase. If the second flash, however, is added somewhat later in time, it can increase the strength of the inhibitory effect in excess of the increment that it causes in excitation. In this case, the double pulse will appear less bright than the single one, because the second burst of stimulation actually gives rise to a larger inhibitory than excitatory effect. Now if an increase in the duration of a light stimulus is thought of as successive additions of brief light pulses in time with no intervening dark intervals, then we can see that, according to this hypothesis, the additional light pulses will at first give rise to increases in excitation over inhibition and the brightness sensation will increase, but for longer durations, when the light pulses are added later in time, then the additional flashes will cause an excess of inhibition, and the brightness will decrease. Hence we have a description of the brightness overshoot, Broca-Sulzer phenomenon.

In the brightness enhancement phenomenon in the flickering light situation, we have said that Bartley reported a maximal enhancement effect for light-dark alternations at a rate of approximately 10 per second. This value holds for an equal light-dark ratio, that is, when the duration of each light flash is equal to the duration of the succeeding dark interval. If the rate of alternation is 10 per second, then each total cycle lasts for 0.1 second. Each light flash lasts for one half of the total cycle, and thus for 0.05 second. This duration of each light flash for maximal brightness enhancement in the flicker situation is of the same order of magnitude as the duration of a single light flash that produces the maximum in the brightness overshoot phenomenon at a fairly high level of flash luminance. According to the results of W. H. Stainton, who published a careful quantitative study of this phenomenon in 1928, these are also the conditions for the maximal brightness overshoot. That is, the ratio of the peak apparent brightness, that occurs at about 0.05 second for this luminance, to the steady brightness seen when the flash continues for approximately 0.2 second, is maximal.

In order to test their theoretical ideas stating that a test flash added in time may give rise either to an increment in excitation or to a stronger inhibition because of the different temporal evolutions of the facilitating and inhibiting processes, Baumgardt and Segal did the following experiment. They devised an apparatus that provided two light fields whose onsets in time could be independently controlled. The duration of each flash was always 10 milliseconds (1 msec. = 0.001 sec.). Both fields were square, and one was smaller than the other and adjusted so as to be centered within the larger one. When these two, 10 milliseconds duration, light fields were flashed simultaneously, thus when the stimulus onsets were adjusted to be the same, then the observer saw a brighter small field centered within a larger less bright one. In this case, of course, the effects of the two superimposed stimuli simply summated, and the brightness of the center area which received light from both flashes was consequently seen as greater than the brightness of the surrounding area which received light from only the one flash filling the larger field. Now, when the onset of the smaller field was delayed, simple summation of the two stimuli no longer occurred. In fact, when the onset of the small field was delayed for 40 to 70 milliseconds after the onset of the larger field, the small square appeared darker, rather than brighter, than the surrounding area. The result is consistent with Baumgardt and Segal's hypothesis that a stimulus presented with just the proper delay after the onset of a prior stimulus will cause an increase in the inhibitory process over the excitatory one. Perceptually a less bright field is seen in the area that receives stimulation from both of the consecutive flashes than in the area that receives stimulation from only the first of the two.

Metacontrast

There is, in fact, a whole visual literature on phenomena closely related to the effect we have been describing. Among these are Bidwell's ghosts and the "pulsative afterimage." Many experiments have been done on the problem of "masking" one stimulus field or pattern by brief exposure to another field at a different moment in time. And there is a related class of visual problems that are generally classified under the title "metacontrast," in which the successive brief stimuli that give rise to masking effects or perceptions of reduced brightness are separated both in time and in space. Many of these experiments become very complicated, and to describe them in any meaningful way would require at least another full chapter. We mention them here only to indicate that all of these temporal phenomena are closely related to one another, and that all of them do indeed reflect the activities of the two opposite response processes of the visual system that we described most generally as action and reaction processes.

BIBLIOGRAPHY

ALPERN, M. Metacontrast. *J. opt. Soc. Amer.*, 1953, **43**, 648–657.

BARTLEY, S. H., PACZEWITZ, G., & VALSI, E. Brightness enhancement and the stimulus cycle. *J. Psychol.*, 1957, **43**, 187–192.

BAUMGARDT, E., & SEGAL, J. Facilitation et inhibition, paramètres de la fonction visuelle. *Anneé Psychol.*, 1947, **43–44**, 54-102.

BIDWELL, S. *Curiosities of Light and Sight*. London: Swan Sonnenschein, 1899.

BROCA, A., & SULZER, D. La sensation lumineuse en fonction du temps. *C. R. Acad. Sci.*, Paris, 1902, **134**, 831–834; 1903, **137**, 944–946.

BRÜCKE, E. Ueber den Nutzeffekt intermittender Netzhautreizungen. *Akad. Wiss. Wien.*, 1864, **49** (2), 128–153.

COHEN, J. Color adaptation of the human eye. *Amer. J. Psychol.*, 1946, **59**, 84–110.

CRAIK, K. J. W. The effect of adaptation on subjective brightness. *Proc. roy. Soc.*, 1940, **B 128**, 232–247.

DITCHBURN, R. W., & GINSBORG, B. L. Involuntary eye movements during fixation. *J. Physiol.*, 1953, **119**, 1–17.

HOCHBERG, J. E., TRIEBEL, W., & SEAMAN, G. Color adaptation under conditions of homogeneous visual stimulation (Ganzfeld). *J. exper. Psychol.*, 1959, **41**, 153–159.

HERING, E. Zur Lehre von Lichtsinne. I. Über successive Lichtinduction. *Sitzber. Akad. der Wissens. Vienna, Math-Naturw. Kl.*, 1872, **66**, 5–24.

HERING, E. *Outlines of a Theory of the Light Sense*. (English Translation, L. M. Hurvich and D. Jameson) Cambridge, Mass.: Harvard, 1964.

JAMESON, D., & HURVICH, L. M. Levels of adaptation and brightness changes during color adaptation. *Science*, 1949, **110**, 92–93.

MCDOUGALL, W. The variation of the intensity of the visual sensation with the duration of the stimulus. *Brit. J. Psychol.*, 1904, **1**, 151–190.

OSGOOD, C. E. *Method and Theory in Experimental Psychology*. New York: Oxford U. P., 1953. Pp. 181–182.

PARSONS, J. H. *An Introduction to the Study of Colour Vision*. (2nd ed.) Cambridge (Eng.): Cambridge U. P., 1924.

PIÉRON, H. Le processus du métacontraste. *J. Psychol.*, Paris, 1935, **32**, 5–24.

PIÉRON, H. Vision in intermittent light. (English Translation, L. M. Hurvich and D. Jameson) In *Contributions to Sensory Physiology* (W. D. Neff, Ed.). New York: Academic Press, 1965.

RIGGS, L. A., RATLIFF, F., CORNSWEET, J. C., & CORNSWEET, T. N. The disappearances of steadily fixated visual test objects. *J. opt. Soc. Amer.*, 1953, 43, 495–501.

STAINTON, W. H. The phenomenon of Broca and Sulzer in foveal vision. *J. opt. Soc. Amer.*, 1928, 16, 26–39.

TROLAND, L. T. *The Principles of Psychophysiology*. Vol. II. *Sensation*. New York: Van Nostrand, 1930.

YARBUS, A. L. The perception of a stabilized retinal image. (In Russian) *Biofizika*, 1956, 1, 435–437.

V

Contrast and Assimilation

THE SUCCESSIVE ADDITION AT CONSECUTIVE MOMENTS in time of increments
of light stimulation can, as we saw in the last chaper, give rise to either of
two opposite effects, one reflecting a process that is associated with an increase in brightness, the other associated with an increase in darkness or
blackness. Both of these processes, one associated with brightness, the
other with darkness, are also in evidence when light stimuli are added simultaneously but in separate spatial locations rather than at separate points
in time. A small dark gray paper chip on a white background looks more
black than the same gray chip on a medium gray background. This is
the well-known phenomenon of simultaneous brightness contrast. Although the two gray paper chips are identical in luminance and appear
identical when viewed against a common, uniform background, the
use of different amounts of background illumination for the two produces two different brightness impressions in the two physically identical
gray test areas; the greater amount of light in the surround in the
case of the white background produces an unmistakable reduction in
apparent brightness or increase in perceived blackness in the test area.
The obverse effect is equally familiar. Two pieces of light gray paper
that have the same photometric luminance specification and that appear
identical against a common background appear different when one is
seen against a black background and the other against a medium gray one.
The light gray on the black background appears brighter and whiter than
the light gray on the medium gray background.

SIMULTANEOUS CONTRAST

Neural Interactions

These perceived changes are physiologically determined. Excitations in all parts of the retinal-neural tissue appear to influence each other. Thus a constant stimulus of fixed luminance which produces a given excitation at a central retinal position has a given brightness appearance associated with it. When the stimulation—and hence the excitation state of the adjacent retinal-neural areas—is changed (by introducing lower or higher luminance surrounds) the excitation state of the central retinal position is changed and the initial stimulus, still of the same fixed luminance, changes its appearance. It will become darker or brighter depending on the luminance and excitation changes in the surrounding areas.

There are many other situations in which contrast is in evidence. For example, late afternoon skylight seen through a window can be made to alternate from light to dark as we flip the switch of the overhead room light that illuminates the wall surrounding the window. Simple desk demonstrations of a similar sort are also possible. If a uniformly illuminated sheet of white paper lying on the table top is looked at through a small aperture cut in a second sheet of white paper held a foot or so above it, the surface seen through the aperture can be made to change its brightness if we tilt the top sheet towards and away from us and thus change the amount of light it reflects. What the contrast mechanism seems to do in all these instances is to magnify the differences in apparent brightness between adjacent areas of different luminances.

But the matter is not all that simple. Suppose that, on a piece of good white bond paper, you were to draw a very fine line in India ink. At a normal viewing distance the line will be only slightly more than just visible. Now, using the same ink, suppose you draw a very thick line on the same paper. There is no question that the thick line appears much blacker than the thin one, even though what you have really done can be described as surrounding the original very thin black line with a strip of black background on both sides. The same effect can be demonstrated if we start with black drawing paper and use white ink rather than black ink on white paper.

If we look very closely, however, at the broad black line, we may see that it is not really uniformly black throughout its entire width. On careful examination, we report that the blackness is deeper at the two outer borders of the broad line than it is in the center. Thus, even though the broad black band produces a blacker overall impression than the thin very narrow black line does, the blackness is greatest at the borders or edges where it is adjacent to the white background and it is least in the center where it is surrounded on both sides by the dark background created by the broad line itself. Thus the contrast problem, which at first glance appears a simple one, is in fact complex. We shall return to some of these complexities of the brightness contrast problem later in this chapter. Let us now look at a rather well-known phenomenon which is cited in most textbooks and discussions of brightness perception.

THE GELB EFFECT

We place an observer in a nearly dark room. Somewhere in his field of view we set up a circular disk made of highly absorbent black paper, or better still, black velvet. We now focus a spotlight on the "black" disk so that the light just fills the disk and nothing else in the room is illuminated. Care has to be taken to shield the spotlight itself so that the observer cannot see the source of the illumination. If the light precisely fills the disk and is sufficiently intense, the observer reports that he sees a glowing white disk against a dark background. If now, with the spotlight still shining on the disk, a small piece of white paper is inserted in the light beam and on top of the larger velvet disk, the observer reports that the entire disk is no longer a glowing white but that it now appears very dark or even black. This demonstration is usually called the Gelb effect, after the investigator who first described it.

SHADOW AND SPOT EFFECTS

Suppose you are walking in a rather dense wood beneath a heavy overlay of leafy branches. On the dimly illuminated foot path, you see a white spot, as if white chalk or lime had been spilled on the soil. As you continue to walk along the path, it becomes obvious that the spot is formed not by something white that has been spilled there, but rather by bright sunlight penetrating through a small gap in the leaf covered branches overhead. Once this fact is recognized, you no longer see the spot as a change in the color and the character of the earth from brown soil to a spot of white material, but only as a place where there is an abrupt increase in illumination caused by the beam of sunlight. Your perception actually changes, and once the change has occurred, it becomes very difficult, if not impossible, to reinstate your first impression that there was an actual change in the material surface of the path.

Most people have also at sometime or other had the experience of trying to dust off a dark spot from a surface or an article of clothing, only later to realize that the surface itself had not changed but that the impression was created by a small shadow cast in that particular form. Again, once we realize that it is only an illumination change produced by a shadow-caster in the path of a light source, it is very difficult to recover the original perception again. What we would now say is that we see a uniform surface but that it is nonuniformly illuminated. The last two examples are cited by E. Hering, who was one of the classical figures in visual perception. The "true" observation, sometimes called the "veridical perception," makes it clear that precisely what we perceive depends to some extent on the information that we have about the total situation and on our interpretation of it.

Explanations; Cognitive Accounts

The Gelb effect that we have described is also ordinarily analyzed as depending on our knowledge of the situation and our interpretation of it. When the source of illumination is hidden from the observer so that he is unaware of it, and the amount of light reaching his eye from the black velvet surface is of sufficiently high luminance, the surface appears to be bright or white. When, however, the small piece of white paper is introduced, it "reveals" the spotlight beam, since it reflects a much greater amount of light to the observer's eye than does the highly absorbing velvet disk. With two different reflectances present in the same illuminated field it becomes possible for the observer to make independent judgments of the surface reflections and the illumination itself, which is presumably of uniform intensity. Thus, the perceived changes are supposedly accounted for in cognitive terms.

This sort of appeal to cognitive factors to explain our perceptions was used most notably by Helmholtz to account for many visual contrast phenomena. For Helmholtz, a cognitive process accounts for the fact that a dark gray paper on a medium gray background looks less black than the same gray paper on a white background. If we had no knowledge of the conditions of illumination in the two instances, we could reasonably attribute the different perceptions to differences in illumination. We might suppose that the brighter background is brighter because of a higher level of illumination. But if it is true that the background is lighter because the illumination has been increased, then the small gray paper on this lighter background should also look lighter. Since it does not become lighter but only the background changes from medium gray to white, this could have come about by reason of the fact that the original small gray paper has been removed from the white background and a blacker one substituted for it. Consequently the small gray paper is perceived as blacker on the white background than on the medium gray one because this appearance is consistent with our judgment of the illumination situation in the two instances. The judgment that presumably determines the brightness perception in cases of this sort is not necessarily, according to Helmholtz, something explicitly reasoned out in the way that we have just presented it but, because of our learning and past experience, occurs automatically as an "unconscious inference" or as an "illusion of judgment."

It is important to note that there is a real distinction here between the unconscious inference explanation as applied to the appearance of the same gray paper on two different backgrounds, and the different perceptions of white or dark spots that depend on information about the conditions of illumination. In the strict unconscious inference view the activities of the visual system itself have nothing to do with the changes in perceived lightness or darkness of a stimulus area whose luminance has remained fixed when the background is changed; our visual perceptions are presumably altered only because of the inferences we make about the external conditions. In the situations described by Hering, the areas in question are perceived as lighter or darker—be they seen as spots or shadows—not because of our interpretations of the situation but because of the way the visual system happens to work as a physiological mechanism that responds to patterns of stimulation. It is the significance alone of the lighter and darker perceptions—whether the areas are perceived as properties of the surfaces or as properties of the illumination—that depends on our interpretation of the total situation.

QUANTITATIVE EXPERIMENTS

As is true of many psychophysical phenomena, alternative explanations are frequently easy to propose and difficult to refute as long as we are dealing only with qualitative observations. When we begin to make our experimental conditions more rigorous and the observations more precise, however, then we find that the variety of acceptable explanations begins immediately to become more restricted. So that we may better understand the interactions that arise when different light stimuli are simultaneously present in an observer's field of view, we turn, therefore, to quantitative experiments that involve such spatial interactions.

We have said that a dark gray paper on a medium gray background looks less black than the same gray paper on a white background. We might restate this observation in a more general way by saying that a light stimulus of circumscribed area will decrease in apparent brightness even though its luminance remains constant as the luminance of a stimulus field that is adjacent to it is continuously increased. One of the first things that we will want to know beyond the gross observation that we have already made is how big is the change that is produced by the adjacent stimulus, and in what way is it related to the varying luminance of the adjacent light field?

Haploscopic Matching Setup

Let us use a haploscopic viewing situation of the sort that was described in the preceding chapter. The optical apparatus is set up in such a way that a test field of given luminance, given size, and given shape is presented to the right eye, and a comparison field of the same size and shape is presented independently to the left eye. If the light beam that provides the comparison stimulus for the left eye is passed through a neutral density wedge of continuously variable transmission, then by adjusting the position of the variable wedge in the comparison beam we can vary the luminance of the comparison field until the comparison field appears identical in brightness to the apparent brightness of the fixed test field that is seen by the right eye. Presumably the physical luminances of the test and comparison fields will be identical in these circumstances provided that the left and right eyes of the observer have the same sensitivity characteristics. We now make provision for a second field, which we may call the contrast inducing field, to be presented next to the square test field and adjust the apparatus so that the inducing field is located immediately adjacent to one side of the test area. If we also make provisions for inserting filters of different densities (or transmissions) and for a second neutral density wedge in the beam of the contrast inducing field, then we shall be able to vary the luminance of the inducing field at will. With a comparison stimulus that can be varied in luminance to match the apparent brightness of the test field, and with an inducing field that can be varied in luminance, we are now in a position to obtain an *indirect* but quantitative answer to the question we raised: how much does the inducing area affect the apparent brightness of the test stimulus, and in what way is the magnitude of this effect related to the inducing luminance? We say the measure is *indirect* because what we can do in this experiment is to determine the luminance of the comparison field that makes this field in its dark surround appear equal in brightness to the appearance of the test area. The changes in matching luminance that constitute the measures of this experiment are not, of course, directly equivalent to changes in perceived brightness, as we already know from the scaling experiments that relate photometric luminance and perceived brightness of light stimuli presented in an otherwise dark surround. What the data do tell us is what luminances are equivalent in apparent brightness for different contrast inducing conditions.

Since our interest in these experiments is to determine the effect of spatial interactions among differently stimulated visual areas we do not want the results to be contaminated by differing states of sensitivity in the two eyes when the stimuli are presented. Care must be taken, therefore, to make sure that the preexposure conditions are carefully controlled. This is commonly achieved by having the observer remain with both eyes shut in a darkened room for some time before the measures begin. We also want to guarantee that the results do not reflect the kinds of fading effects that occur with continued exposure of long durations, and consequently the apparatus must be set up in such a way as to provide for fairly short exposure durations of the test and inducing fields to the right eye and of the comparison field to the left. Between the exposures that last, say, about 1 second, adequate rest intervals in the dark must be provided before another test exposure is made.

Experimental Results

If we do such an experiment, making sure to observe all the precautions that we have just stated, then we may obtain functions of the sort shown in Fig. 5. Here, on the abscissa we have plotted the logarithm

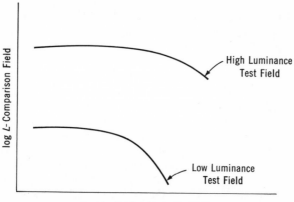

Figure 5. Effect of variation in contrast inducing luminance on matches to test fields of different luminances.

of the luminance of the contrast inducing field, and on the ordinate the logarithm of the luminance of the comparison field that is required to match the test field of fixed luminance when each of the series of inducing luminances is presented next to the test area. If we look at the upper curve in the figure, (for a test field of relatively high luminance) we see that the change in matching luminance that is required is small for a fairly wide range of inducing luminance values, and that the change increases as the inducing luminance is raised to still higher values. The lower curve on the same graph represents the expected findings from a repetition of this same experiment but this time for a test field that is maintained at a lower level of luminance than in the first instance. The levels of inducing luminance are the same for both curves and we see that in both instances the comparison luminance decreases at the higher levels of inducing luminance which implies, of course, that the test field of fixed luminance appears increasingly darker.

The experimental data obtained in such experiments make it quite clear that the simplest relation that has been proposed for such effects cannot be valid. The most simple relation predicts that the inducing stimulus would decrease the effectiveness of the test stimulus by a factor that is proportional to the strength of the inducing field itself. Thus:

$$L'_t = L_t/kL_i \tag{1}$$

or

$$\log L'_t = \log L_t - \log (kL_i). \tag{2}$$

Here, L_t is the measured luminance of the test field, L_i is the measured luminance of the inducing field, L'_t is the equivalent luminance of the test field, measured in our experiments by luminance of the comparison field, L_m, that matches the apparent brightness of the test area. Represented graphically, this relation is described for a series of test luminances by a series of parallel straight lines with negative slope; hence it clearly cannot represent the curvilinear functions shown in Fig. 5.

Hess and Pretori Apparatus

The prototype of the experimental setup for quantitative investigations of contrast phenomena is the classical one used by Hess and Pretori in 1894. The essence of the apparatus consists of four separate and independently variable light beams. The four light sources are indicated in Figs. 6A and 6B by the letters S_l, S'_l, S_r and S'_r. The light from S_l is reflected from the diagonally positioned diffusing surface labelled D_l, passes through the aperture in front of it, and continues on in the direction of the observer's eye. The light from S'_l is reflected from the diagonal surface that contains this aperture, and thereafter follows the same direction towards the observer's eye. The light paths from the sources S_r and S'_r on the right-hand side of the apparatus are similar to those on the left.

With an apparatus of this sort we can independently control the test and comparison areas and their surrounds, which can be of any desired size or luminance level.

The separate luminances of the four independent beams can be controlled by the use of filters of different densities in the light paths, by

A

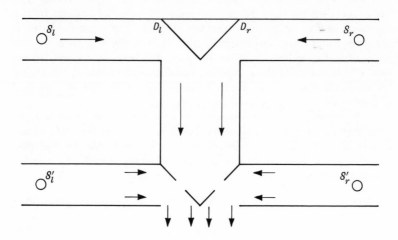

B

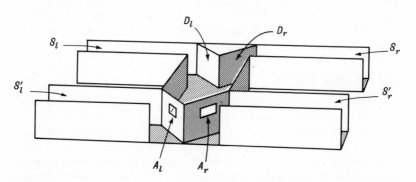

Figure 6. Hess and Pretori apparatus. Schematic diagram and perspective sketch.

neutral wedges of varying density, or, as in the original design, by varying the distances of the four light sources from the diffusing surfaces and thus from the observer's eye. For this purpose the sources are mounted on tracks, or optical rails, so that they can be moved readily, and their positions read from appropriately placed scales. In this way the variation in luminance approximates the inverse square law. This way of varying luminance requires a good deal of physical space, but if the space is available, it has the advantage that the color of the fields is unaffected by the luminance control. As we pointed out in Chapter I, most so-called neutral density filters and wedges that are commercially available actually cause a slight yellowing of the field as the density is increased to decrease the luminance.

In an apparatus such as that shown in the diagram, the left and right fields may be observed either monocularly, as in the original Hess and Pretori experiments, or binocularly. By continuing the vertical divider in front of the apparatus, the fields can be maintained separately for the left and right eyes of the observer, and the observations become what we have called haploscopic.

Alternative Measures of Contrast Effects

There are alternative ways in which measures of contrast effects can be obtained with such an apparatus. The two smaller fields provided by the left and right sources can first be matched in apparent brightness, then a specified contrast inducing luminance can be added to the surround field on the right by adjusting the source S'_r to some fixed level. The luminance of the left source S_l is then adjusted to match the apparent brightness of the smaller right field and thus to compensate for the brightness change on the right caused by introduction of the inducing field. For such measures the beam from S'_l is not used at all, and the comparison field provided by S_l is always seen in dark surroundings. If the experiment is done in this way, it is usually found that, when the luminance of the inducing field S'_r has been increased beyond a certain level, the test area S_r takes on a very black appearance. This blackness cannot be matched by the source S_l in its dark surround no matter how much we reduce the intensity of S_l. The induced blackness on the right is simply darker or blacker than the total absence of light, and it can never be matched unless another inducing field is introduced next to the comparison field illuminated by S_l. It is important therefore to make provision for a fourth beam on the left, comparison side in order to be able to explore a wide range of inducing luminances on the right side.

Another way that contrast measures can be obtained is to set the luminances of the test and inducing fields on the right at some fixed set of levels and then, at each of a series of different luminances of the comparison field, determine the luminance of the comparison inducing field S'_l that must be used in order to make each of the series of comparison luminances match the fixed test field on the right. It was measures of this sort that Hess and Pretori actually obtained in their early experiments.

Hess and Pretori Findings

In one series they found that when the small test field and its surround were kept fixed and the small comparison field was set at a series
of luminance levels, the luminance of the comparison contrast-inducing
field had to be increased in direct proportion to the increased luminance
of the comparison area itself if the latter was to appear equivalent in
brightness to the apparent brightness of the fixed test field. For this one
particular set of surround and test field conditions, the increased brightness in the comparison field that accompanied an increase in its luminance
could be directly offset by proportionately increasing the luminance of
its surround.

By proportionally increasing the luminance of the surround, the *ratio*
of the comparison field luminance to its surround luminance is restored
to the same value in each instance. This ratio expression reminds us again
of the general expressions for the results of scaling experiments that compare the growth of apparent brightness with the growth of photometric
luminance. There too, the apparent brightness function was stated to
depend on the *ratio* of the test luminance to the background luminance
(see Chapter I, Equations 2 and 3).

The constant ratio of comparison to surround luminance was obtained, however, for only a single set of test and surround luminance
values in the right half of the viewing field; when the test field was
about 20 to 30 mL and the surround approximately 100 mL, direct proportionality was obtained. The millilambert values used here represent
approximately correct ratios only. Hess and Pretori's measures were reported in photometric units that are no longer in current use, and it is
difficult to convert them precisely to the standard photometric units
that are in use today. Although it is easier to discuss their results in terms
of luminance units, we must keep in mind that the numbers we use do not
actually represent the precise luminance values of the original experiment.

When the luminance of the test field was increased to about ten times
its original value, say, 300 mL, and the luminance of the surround reduced to about one tenth, 10 mL, then the variation required in the comparison surround at different levels of comparison field luminance to
make the comparison field equivalent in brightness to the fixed test
brightness was no longer directly proportional to the increase in comparison field luminance. For this particular set of test and surround
values, the increase in the luminance of the comparison surround had to
be disproportionately greater than the increase in the luminance of the
comparison field in order for all comparison field luminances to have the
same equivalent brightness. Furthermore, when the luminance of the test
field was decreased and the level of its surround increased, then once

again as the matching comparison field was increased in luminance the luminance of its surround had to be increased to produce an equivalent brightness impression between the small test and comparison fields. But in this case the comparison surround had to be raised in luminance by a somewhat lower factor than the relative increase of the comparison field luminance in order to produce the same brightness impression at all comparison field levels. It is clear that if we consider all of the data the apparent brightness is not always the same function of the simple ratio between the test and background luminance levels. The situation is somewhat more complicated, as we shall see when we come, in the next chapter, to discuss the problem of brightness constancy.

Size of Inducing Area; Difficulties for Cognitive Explanations

What of the size of the inducing area? If we keep a test field constant in size and in luminance and a small contrast inducing field is progressively increased in size until it completely surrounds the test area, we should certainly expect that it would have a progressively greater effect on the apparent brightness of the enclosed test field. Will this also be true if we increase the area of the contrast inducing stimulus without actually surrounding more of the test field? We can check this in an experiment where the test field is a square, and the inducing field is contiguous with one side of the test square. The inducing field is placed next to the test area along a vertical edge, the vertical dimension of the inducing area is kept constant, and its width can be varied from a very narrow rectangular strip up to a square area that has the same dimensions as the test stimulus. Experiments of precisely this sort have been carried out, and the results show that the changes in matching luminance for a series of inducing luminances of increasing levels are considerably smaller when the inducing field is very narrow than they are when it has the same width, as well as the same height, as the test field. The darkening effect of the contrast inducing stimulus is clearly greater as the size of the stimulus is increased at any given luminance level.

If we think back to the kind of interpretative account that was offered as a possible explanation for the fact that the same test stimuli looked brighter or darker when seen in darker or brighter surrounds, respectively, we remember that in essence it said the following. When the surround brightens, the observer presumably infers that the overall level of illumination on both the background and test stimulus has been increased, but since the test stimulus itself does not indeed increase in luminance, then the way in which this might occur would be for a different test stimulus of lower reflectance to be substituted for it. Consequently, the inferred lower reflectance of the test paper could account for its appearing to have darkened. As we said, it is difficult to refute or confirm such an explanation on the basis of general qualitative descriptions alone. If we try to apply this sort of explanation, however, to the results of a precisely controlled quantitative experiment which show that as the width of the contrasting field is progressively increased there is a systematic increase in its darkening effect on the test stimulus, we run aground of serious obstacles. It is difficult to work out a rational explanation in terms of possible changes in overall illumination and test area reflectance that might have been unconsciously inferred by an observer to account for the progressive increase in darkening effect. To be consistent we would have to say that an observer infers that the illumination has been increased when the size of the contrast inducing field is increased. There is nothing in our everyday visual experience on which such an inference could be based.

Bimodal Process Explanation

We can, however, take this result as another indication of the bimodal nature of the visual system's responses to light stimulation. In this instance, the light stimulus in a given test area seems to evoke a brightening action; another brightening action is evoked next to it in the visual field upon the introduction of a second white field. But when this occurs the second stimulus also brings about an opposite, darkening reaction in the adjacent test area that was initially present alone. We should remember, of course, that these interactions must be mutual and reciprocal ones. Because of the particular measures made in these experiments, the effect is almost always discussed as the effect of the contrast inducing field on the test area. A moment's reflection, however, will suggest that had we simply chosen to label the two fields differently, the apparent brightness of the contrast inducing field might be the perception of interest, and it clearly would also be affected by the presence next to it of the test stimulus of given luminance and size.

Border Contrast Effects; Mach Rings

If we want a vividly striking demonstration of contrast effects, we can set up a stimulus situation where contours or lines are perceived in the visual field by contrast action even though no such lines actually exist in the stimulus pattern itself. The effect is most easily seen by rotating at a fairly rapid speed on a color wheel a white disk that has inked on it a good black figure of the sort shown in Fig. 7. In this figure, the center portion of the disk is totally blackened. Starting at the inner point labelled *a* and moving out along the radius, an increasing amount of the white disk is exposed, and at the inflection point in the star-shaped figure

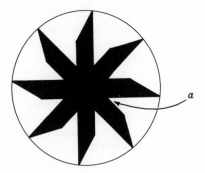

Figure 7. Figure used to produce Mach rings.

there is a second, more rapid, increase in exposed white area. This continues out to the perimeter of the disk where the area is nearly all white. When this disk is rotated rapidly, the average luminance reflected from it will be very low in the center. From the point on the radius where the white background is first exposed the average luminance will gradually increase, and there will be another more rapid graded increase in average luminance starting at the point on the radius where the sharp bends occur. If our brightness perceptions simply followed the average stimulus luminance gradient when this figure is set into rotation at a sufficiently rapid speed to eliminate flicker, then the description given in luminance terms should also provide a qualitative description of the apparent brightness gradient that we perceive on the disk. But this is not so. When we observe the disk in rapid rotation, what we actually see are distinct dark or black rings at those positions along the radius that correspond to the sharp bends in the star-shaped figure. It is as if two circles had been drawn with black ink at these locations. The areas on both sides of the perceived border line tend to appear rather uniform in brightness, as if in these areas an averaging were occurring along a radial extent even though the actual luminance is continuously increasing from the center beyond a to the perimeter. But where an area of higher luminance surrounds an area of lower luminance, the contrast darkening action of the visual system is so great that it actually produces a dark border line that seems to separate the two areas. The obverse is true if the starlike figure is white and the background black. The brightness relations are, of course, reversed throughout, and here we see a series of uniform areas of increasing darkness from center to periphery, and separated, in this figure, by white or light circular bands or rings.

The phenomenon of a perceived contour where none actually exists in the physical stimulus is called a Mach ring or band. It is named after E. Mach, the famous physicist who explored this property of our visual brightness perceptions in a series of studies published in the eighteen-sixties. Although the kinds of stimulus configurations that give rise to the most striking Mach ring effects are most conveniently set up on rotating color wheels, they are by no means dependent on the rotation itself. Mach rings can be observed equally well in still photographs taken of such spinning disks. Mach himself took such photographs to make this point and also cited other instances of the phenomenon where no physical motion is involved. One example is a sharply defined roof top seen against the sky as background, a circumstance that will reveal an enhanced contour line if carefully observed.

Explanation of These Effects

The most striking aspect of Mach ring demonstrations is, of course, the unexpected appearance of the dark or bright rings or contours. But the fact that each intermediate region between the contours appears to be approximately uniform in apparent brightness, even though the luminance actually varies radially in these regions, is equally important in the functioning of the visual brightness mechanism. In his analysis of the phenomenon, Mach recognized that its basis lay in the mutual interactions that occur among the physiological activities of neighboring parts of the visual system, and he generalized the result of such physiological interaction in the following way. He said that the visual system is so organized as to emphasize perceptually a deviation from the mean of the stimulation in the environment. The locations at which dark rings appear are not physically less luminous than the neighboring parts on both sides but the luminance at these places is less than the mean luminance of the immediately adjacent parts. And it is this deviation from the mean that is emphasized by the visual processes of brightness perception. On the other hand, says Mach, a continuous change in luminance is scarcely effective, as long as the luminance of each particular point corresponds to the average of the adjacent points. If we have a continuous and constant rate of increase in luminance across a part of a light surface, then the luminance at each point will be the same as the mean of the slightly lower luminance on one side of it and the slightly higher luminance on the other side. It is only at the location where the *rate of change* in luminance undergoes an increase or a decrease that a significant deviation from the mean of the adjacent luminances occurs, and it is at this location that the accentuation occurs and a contour is perceived. The result of such an organization is, says Mach, that "small differences are slurred over by the retina, and larger differences stand out with disproportionate clearness. The retina schematizes and caricatures."

Since the spatial luminance gradient itself, or the rate of change in luminance from one position to the next, seems not to be appreciated by the visual system as a brightness gradient, but only a change in the slope of the spatial luminance gradient is visually effective, Mach generalized the phenomenon mathematically by saying that the brightness perception depends on the second derivative, or the rate of change in the slope, of the spatial luminance distribution.

ROLE OF CONTRAST MECHANISM

It is not immediately apparent that there would be any useful function in our commerce with the real world for a system that produces apparent contours or lines where none exist in the real world. In fact we are aware of instances where the interpretation of X-ray photographs was made extremely difficult because of the appearance of such Mach rings in the photographs that could not be attributed to any known physical structure in the original. Only after a physical analysis of the film densities showed that there were no sharp lines of greater density in the film at the positions where the black lines appeared in the visual brightness distribution was it realized that the problem was a perceptual, and not a diagnostic, one. But the overall value to vision of such a brightness and darkness enhancement mechanism, even though it may lead us astray on occasion, becomes clear when we know something about the optical characteristics of the human eye and their shortcomings.

Image Formation by the Eye

Light from an external object enters the eye through the transparent cornea, passes through the pupil whose opening is delimited by the iris, goes through the crystalline lens behind the pupil, and is absorbed at the back of the eyeball by the sensitive retina. The space between the cornea and the lens is filled with a watery liquid called the aqueous humour, and the space between the lens and the retina is filled with a more viscous liquid called the vitreous humour. It is primarily due to the action of the curved surfaces of the cornea and the crystalline lens that divergent light rays coming from the various points on an object are converged to form the object's image on the surface of the retina. In one sense, the dioptric mechanism of the eye is a remarkably good one, because it is equipped with automatic adjustments that operate through a neuromuscular feedback loop to change the characteristics of the system as the characteristics of the light entering the eye change. Thus, when the amount of light markedly increases or decreases, the iris muscles react to narrow or widen the diameter of the pupillary opening and in this way to restrict the total range of illumination to which the retina is exposed. The ciliary muscles alter the shape of the crystalline lens to change its focusing properties as the eye is directed toward nearer or farther objects. This focusing mechanism controls what is usually called the accommodation of the eye. The eye is frequently described as having characteristics similar to those of a camera; and with respect to these control features, it is like a very expensive camera with automatic feedback from a light meter to control the size of the aperture in front of the lens. It also has its built-in range finder with automatic focusing adjustment for the appropriate object distance.

But like all optical devices, even the most costly, the optical system of the eye is not a perfect one. A point in outer space is not imaged on the retina as a true point, but rather as a somewhat more diffuse area usually called a blur circle. In any optical system, the size of the blur circle depends on a variety of factors, and is influenced by the amounts of the various aberrations inherent in the system. The most common of these are chromatic aberrations, which lead to colored fringes around the edges of images formed by white light, and spherical aberrations, which produce distortions in the shape of the image from the center to its outer edges. In the human eye, these aberrations are actually quite large. Moreover, as light penetrates the eye, a good deal of it is dispersed in more or less random fashion as it passes through the various media and undergoes multiple reflections from the various surface boundaries. This optical process distributes a diffuse overlay of so-called stray light over the entire image plane. The net effect of all these imperfections in the optical system of the eye is that the images formed on the retina are not, in fact, of very good quality. They are not extremely sharp, like, for example, the shadow cast by an object in direct sunlight, but more like the relatively blurred shadow of the same object when the source of illumination is diffuse skylight and not the direct sun. Nevertheless, we do not see the outlines of well-delineated objects as indistinct or somewhat blurred in the way the optical system of our eye actually images them on the retina, but rather we see good sharp edges. That the contours we see are sharp despite the nonsharp retinal images comes about because of the same border contrast enhancement that gives rise to Mach bands and rings even when they are not present in the physical stimulus.

Sharpening Effect of Contrast Mechanism

If it were not for the sharpening effect of the brightness contrast mechanism, then our visual acuity would be much inferior to what it is. Actually, we can visually resolve the retinal image of a gap in a line, or a separation between adjacent lines on a very fine grid, that is smaller than the diameter of an individual foveal cone. Our visual acuity is without doubt considerably aided by the fact that our eyes are constantly undergoing very small tremor movements even when we are attempting to fixate very steadily. Because of these slight tremors, the difference in light stimulation across the gap in a line is presented successively and alternatingly to a series of neighboring retinal receptors. But even with the advantage afforded by these eye movements, it seems safe to say that it is unlikely that we would be able to resolve the fine detail that we can unless the contrast sharpening mechanism of spatial interaction were also operating to convert the blurred edges of the light image on the retina to the sharp edges that we actually perceive.

Still another way to observe the border contrast effect is by the use of a gray scale. To make such a scale, select, say, five separate strips of paper that vary from the deepest black through three intermediate progressively lighter shades of gray up to the whitest paper that can be found. Fairly wide strips of these papers are cut and arranged serially one beside the other on a stiff backing, the papers are carefully butted so that the cut edges themselves cannot be seen, and the scale is placed under good illumination at some distance from the observer. The different strips do not appear uniform across their entire width. As we look from the darkest strip toward the lightest, a darker edge shows up at each boundary between the darker and next lighter strip, and a lighter edge is seen at the border where it is next to a strip darker than itself. Compared to its mid-portion, each strip is lighter at one border and darker at the other. The edge effect is accentuated in such a gray scale because the contrast effect is in the opposite direction at each of the two borders of a strip. One can eliminate these effects by making a mask of gray paper which has a cutout exactly the size of a single strip. If only a single strip is viewed through the aperture in the mask the alternating light and dark border contrast effect disappears.

We saw earlier that a contrast darkening effect produced by exposure of a contrast inducing light field next to a test area depends systematically on the size of the contrast inducing field. The border contrast phenomena suggest that the effect is greatest at the location where the areas of different luminance are contiguous and that it falls off very rapidly across the width of each strip. If this were not so, then the presence of a darker band next to a lighter one would bring about not a brightening only at the boundary between the two, but a uniform lightening across the whole of the strip in question.

Separation Between Stimulus Fields

The precise way in which the brightness contrast effect depends on the amount of separation between two interacting stimulus areas can be measured by the use of apparatus and procedures of the sort that we described earlier. We can again make haploscopic brightness matches to a test field on the right side by means of a variable comparison field on the left, but now we introduce a contrast inducing field of fixed size and luminance at various distances from the test area. The amount of change in apparent brightness of the test field will, of course, depend systematically on the level of luminance of the contrast inducing field. For a given level of contrast inducing luminance, however, measurements of the equivalent comparison luminance in such experiments make it clear that the contrast effect does indeed decrease rapidly with an increase in separation between the test and inducing areas. Leibowitz, Mote, and Thurlow, in some experiments conducted in 1953, found that the contrast effect diminished to a minimal value when the separation between the test and inducing fields was approximately twice as large as the size of each of the stimulus areas itself. They used very small test and inducing fields, areas that subtended an angle of about 30′ at the eye (an object 2 mm in height at a distance of about 250 cm from the eye). We should remember, however, that the precise separation at which the minimal contrast is produced depends on the absolute and relative sizes of the stimulus areas in question, and we wish to emphasize here only that the effect is most marked at the nearer distances of the interacting fields, that it drops off very rapidly, and that it gradually approaches a minimal effectiveness at larger separations.

ROLE OF MEMORY, EXPERIENCE, AND INTERPRETATION

If the various contrast phenomenon we have been describing are all manifestations of the fundamental mode of operation of the visual mechanism, should we then conclude that memory, experience, and interpretations of the stimulus conditions have no effect whatsoever on our visual perceptions? What of the observations made by Hering on light spots and shadows that we cited in the introduction to this chapter? When we see the lighter area on the path in the woods and perceive it as spilled chalk, then we would probably say that it looks white if we were asked to describe the brightness of the surface at this position. If, on the other hand, we have already observed that there is a shaft of sunlight hitting the ground at that position, then we would probably say that the surface is dark brown, just as we would describe the rest of the soil of the foot path. The difference between these two descriptions of our brightness perceptions is the difference between light and dark.

Ambiguous Situations; Instructions and Observer's Set

Very often in perceptual experiments where different results are obtained and are described as changes brought about by changes in the "meaning" of the stimulus situation, the effects are actually produced by factors which *do indeed change the stimulus situation* itself as well as the observer's interpretation of it. In this example, however, the change in our description is not associated with any change whatsoever in the pattern of light stimulation incident on our retina, but results exclusively from a change in our interpretation of the causes of that pattern of light stimulation. If we set up a situation in the laboratory that approximated the outdoor one and asked an observer to vary the luminance of a comparison stimulus to match the spot in question, we might get very different answers for the matching luminance value. If the observer saw the spot as a white surface, then he would presumably set the luminance of the matching stimulus at a relatively high value. But if he saw the surface as dark with a high level of illumination incident on it, then he might try to match the dark surface, or he might, on the other hand, try to match the brightness impression that results from the combination of the surface reflectance and the illumination incident on it. Depending on which of these alternatives the observer chose, we could get very different matching luminance values. He could, of course, make a match which is a compromise between these two alternatives. In any event, it seems obvious that with this kind of experimental setup and a potentially ambiguous external stimulus situation, when the observer is asked to match the comparison field to the test area the instructions that he is given will be of paramount importance. There are, in fact, many reports in the literature on visual perception of different series of matching data that were obtained simply by giving different instructions to the observer and thus changing his "set." And it has often been reported that in situations of the kind we have been describing observers can match either the illumination or the surface reflectance. There is no reason to doubt that they can do so. Hochberg and Beck have reported that comparable situations and effects can occur when a stimulus field is set up in which there is ambiguity with respect to the shapes or orientations of the various stimulus areas and their apparent depths.

Evans' Experiments

The Hess-Pretori apparatus diagramed in Fig. 6 can be used to illustrate this. As employed by Hess and Pretori in their original contrast experiments, the apparatus was totally enclosed and placed at such a distance from the observer that the test and comparison areas and their surrounds all appeared to lie in a single frontal plane. Between observations, the front of the apparatus was occluded by two cardboard sheets butted along the center line, the observer saw the stimulus fields only during brief test exposures made by drawing aside the cardboard shields, and for each observation his eyes were directed toward a point on the dividing line between the left and right halves of the total field. In his book, *An Introduction to Color*, R. M. Evans reports observations made with an approximate duplication of the Hess-Pretori apparatus. However, the observer was located closer to the viewing fields, fixation was not controlled, no shields were used between observations, and there was some illumination in the experimental room at all times. Under these circumstances, it is possible to see that the smaller test and comparison fields are indeed located at some distance behind the left and right surround fields and that they are seen through apertures in the two surrounds. It is also possible to see that the left and right surround fields do not lie in a single plane perpendicular to the observer's line of sight, but that they are actually positioned at right angles to each other. Evans was able to instruct his observers to consider the two adjacent surround fields as forming a single flat plane and the test and comparison areas as located behind this plane at a more remote distance. Alternatively, he could instruct his observers to consider the surround fields to represent the two sides of a cube looked at on edge, and to see the test and comparison fields as separate squares of paper pasted on two sides of the cube. With the second set of instructions, when the two surround fields have very different levels of luminance, the stimulus conditions could be such that both surround surfaces are of equal reflectance but one face of the cube is oriented more favorably toward the incident illumination while the other is in partial shadow. If the test area, set at a lower luminance than its surround, is considered to be a gray paper on, say, the more strongly illuminated side of the cube, then the observer can try to produce a brightness appearance in the comparison area that would be equivalent to a gray paper of the same reflectance—but a gray paper viewed in shadow, the way the surround is seen on that "shadowed" side of the cube. Evans found that with his two different sets of instructions he was able to obtain very consistent data for the comparison matching luminance from observer to observer, and that the values obtained under the two different instructions were indeed very different. In this experimental situation, also, the different results do not reflect any change whatsoever in the pattern of light stimulation on the observer's retina. Here too they reflect only a difference in the observer's interpretation of the total pattern of stimulation. When the observer is instructed to regard the two surround surfaces as the two sides of a cube made of the same material and of the same reflectance, and to consider the test and comparison areas as surfaces pasted on the two sides of the cube, there is also the implied instruction that in making his match the observer is to produce a comparison field that appears to have the same reflectance characteristics as the reflectance of the test field. If one looks like gray paper, make the other look like the same gray paper, and so forth. In the other instruction, when the observer is told to regard the two surrounds as two different reflectances lying in a single flat plane, and to treat the test and comparison fields as two different luminous fields located behind the surround plane, by implication the observer is being instructed this time to match the comparison to the test field in apparent brightness rather than to match the reflectance of the surface seen in a different illumination. It is not surprising that instructions which have such different implications are responsible for the different comparison luminances that the observers produce in the two cases.

Matching by Mixtures of Pigments

Perhaps we can clarify what is going on by using still another example. Suppose you are looking at an expanse of painted wall that is illuminated by sunlight coming from a window. Suppose further that the location of the window with respect to the wall is such that part of the wall is in full light and another part of it is strongly shadowed. You, as the observer, have a palette and a variety of oil pigments which you are easily able to mix. You are asked to produce a color on the palette for a paint that will match the wall. Most people have no difficulty in accepting this instruction to produce a single paint, which then presumably could be brushed on the wall for a perfect reproduction of the original surface. What you do in this case is match with the mixture of pigments on the palette the reflectance of the paint that is already on the wall so that your mixture will look the same as the wall now does.

Does the fact that you select only a single paint for the match mean that you see the brightness of the wall as uniform throughout? Apparently not, for if you are now asked to mix paint in order to paint a representational picture of the wall as it appears to you, then you will need at least two pigment mixtures of two different reflectances, one for the wall area in full sunlight and the other for the wall area in shadow. The point we are trying to make is that when a change in instructions produces a change in the observer's match, it is not so much that the observer now *sees* a different array of brightnesses in the visual field and consequently alters his matches, but rather that, *seeing the same array of brightnesses*, he *does* something different in the two situations depending on what it is he is being asked to do or what it is he thinks he is being asked to do.

GELB EFFECT RECONSIDERED

Knowledge of Illumination

We are now in a position to return to the Gelb effect. We remember that this phenomenon is the white appearance of a rotating black disk when it is illuminated by shining a concealed spotlight on it alone while the rest of the room is either very dimly illuminated or totally dark. As soon as a small piece of white paper is introduced in front of the rotating disk so that it is also illuminated by the spotlight, the disk no longer appears white, but rather, blackish. The illumination on the disk has not, of course, been changed, and the usual explanation of the changed perception is that by introducing the white paper we reveal to the observer the existence and nature of the spotlight illumination. We consequently make it possible for him to judge the reflectance of the rotating surface. Up to the moment that the white paper is introduced, if the experiment is carefully set up and there are no telltale cues to disclose the presence of the spotlight, the observer has no basis on which to make a judgment of the reflectance. This is essentially the point that Gelb made in his report of this phenomenon in 1929, and he wished especially to demonstrate that the level of illumination cannot be judged unless the observer can simultaneously see at least two surfaces of different reflectance that are illuminated by the same source. A discussion of the Gelb effect in these terms can also be found in Woodworth and Schlosberg's *Experimental Psychology*.

It is important to note, however, that the changed perceptions of the Gelb phenomenon differ in an important respect from the instances that we have just described in which the pattern of retinal stimulation remains constant and only the observer's "set" or his interpretation of the situation changes. In Gelb's demonstration, the rotating disk always appears whitish when the spotlight illuminates it exclusively, and it always appears blackish when the white paper is introduced. The fact that the presence of the white paper does more than "reveal" the nature of the illumination is indicated by the observation that even after the paper has been introduced and the observer has seen the whitish disk become blackish in appearance, whenever the paper is removed again, the whitish appearance of the disk is reinstated. Knowledge of the illumination does not suffice to make the disk look black if the white paper is not actually a part of the stimulus field. The fact that the white paper must be present strongly suggests that the action of the physiological brightness contrast mechanism itself must have something to do with this effect and that it cannot be attributed to cognitive or interpretive factors exclusively.

Stewart's Experiment

If the white paper does in fact act as a contrast inducing field, in addition to or instead of its presumed role as a cue to the special illumination conditions, can we demonstrate this experimentally? We have just discussed the fact that contrast inducing fields have measurable effects on the apparent brightness of test areas and that these effects depend systematically on the size of the contrast inducing field and also on its position with respect to the test area. What if in the Gelb situation, we were to vary the size of the white paper that is introduced as well as its position on the disk? In some experiments reported in 1959 Stewart did exactly this. His apparatus included a divided chamber with color wheels placed on both the left and right sides. A binocular septum was provided so that the observer saw the right-hand field only with his right eye and the left-hand field only with his left eye. On the color wheel on the right side the test disk was painted black, and a spotlight beam just filled the disk uniformly. In the left-hand side of the apparatus the color wheel was equipped with a variable measuring disk made up of an adjustable black sector (painted with the same black paint as the test disk) and an adjustable sector that was painted white. The walls of the box and the table top on which it rested were covered with black cloth. These black surroundings reflected only a small fraction of the diffuse light that served to illuminate the variable measuring disk. Small contrast producing stimuli were cut from the same material that was used for the variable white sector of the measuring disk, and each of these was supported by invisible threads. A concealed adjustable framework to which the threads were attached made it possible to introduce the contrast inducing stimulus at different positions with respect to the test area, and different sizes of inducing stimuli were also used. When the measuring disk was rotated at a fairly rapid speed, a series of achromatic colors of different brightnesses could be produced that varied from black through a whole series of intermediate grays to white. The observer's task was to report when the variable measuring disk had the same brightness appearance as the test disk. These matches were made when only the test disk was illuminated by the spotlight, and when each size of contrasting white stimulus was introduced at each of a series of different positions. Stewart found that the appearance of the Gelb disk did not simply vary from white in the absence of a contrasting field to black when the contrasting field was present. This, of course, is the usual qualitative description given of the Gelb effect. Rather he found that the test disk was matched in brightness by a series of different grays (different ratios of black to white sectors) in the comparison field, depending on the size of the contrast field and its position. The Gelb disk looked blackest when the contrast stimulus of largest area was introduced, and it looked increasingly more gray and less black when, at the same position, the contrasting field was progressively reduced in size to one quarter of its largest diameter. Moreover, for any given size of contrasting stimulus, the Gelb disk looked blackest when the contrasting stimulus was introduced nearest to its center and looked increasingly more gray and less black as the contrasting stimulus was moved progressively farther from the center of the disk toward one edge of it.

The results of Stewart's experiment make it quite clear that the

Gelb effect depends on more than simply a change in the viewer's interpretation of the stimulus situation. It also depends, at least in part, on the nature of the spatial interactions in the visual system itself, interactions that give rise to what we can safely assume are physiologically based brightness contrast effects. Another observation that was made in Stewart's experiment was that the darkening effect induced by the contrasting stimulus was not uniform over the entire surface of the disk; the strongest darkening occurred in the immediate region of the contrasting stimulus, and lesser degrees of darkening occurred at more remote positions. Again we have here a distance dependent phenomenon that is consistent with other measures of visual interaction effects.

SUMMATION AND AVERAGING EFFECTS

In this discussion of spatial interactions and their effects on brightness perception, we have concentrated primarily on the contrast aspect, the mechanism that serves to heighten the perceived effects of stimulus differences. What of other effects of spatial interaction; that is, those that resemble something more like summation or averaging across differently stimulated areas? We have already mentioned this in describing the Mach ring phenomenon, where the contrast mechanism operates to accentuate stimulus differences and to produce contours visually where they do not exist as contours in the stimulus pattern itself. We noted that the intermediate areas bounded by the contours do not show a gradient of brightness such as can be demonstrated in the light image itself; rather the brightness appears to be more or less uniform throughout an area where the luminance *gradient*, not the luminance, is constant. We know that we can represent shading in a sketch very effectively by use of the pointillist technique: a closely spaced mosaic of pencil dots on a white paper will be seen in the sketch as an area in shadow. In the same way, halftone reproductions made by conventional printing methods achieve their tones of white through grays to black by the density of black dots printed. The technique is most effective and subtle when the dot size and spacing are of very fine grain. If we recall the discussion of spatial integration over very small stimulated areas of the retina in connection with the variables that affect the determination of a light threshold, it seems likely that the same integrative capacity of the visual system is the primary factor that operates here. We say that the mosaic of dots is beyond the limit of spatial resolution of the system, which is another way of saying that the individual dots and the elements of white background separating them are so small that groups of them fall within the limits of spatial integration of the eye. Indeed, if we examine a halftone reproduction under a magnifying glass, we see the separate individual black dots and their different spacings in the differently shaded areas. Or, in an art museum, if we walk up very close to a pointillist painting, the effectiveness of the painting as a work of art is lost, and what we see is a meaningless mosaic of different colors.

Thus we might summarize the situation by saying that the visual brightness mechanism, by mutual opponent interaction among activities in neighboring physiological elements, accentuates differences in response in these elements to small differences in stimulus luminance. But these opponent interactions are not the only ones that occur: if the stimulus luminance differences in adjacent elements are too small and uniformly graded from one element to the next, or if the sizes of the different stimulus elements are too small to be resolved by the eye, then the activities in neighboring elements seem to pool rather than to oppose each other.

ASSIMILATION PHENOMENA

Bezold Spreading Effect

But we can observe still other stimulus situations in which the grain of the stimulus pattern is not reduced to such an extent that we cannot resolve it, and yet we see not a contrast effect, but rather its opposite. The opposite of contrast, namely, an effect called assimilation, can be demonstrated with very simple materials. One needs only a piece of gray paper, India ink, white ink, a pen with a good fine point, and a straight edge. The gray paper is divided in two halves, on one half cross-hatching is ruled with the black ink, and on the other half cross-hatching of the same spacing and thickness is ruled with the white ink. If the cross-hatching is not too coarse, it is likely that the assimilation effect will be rather strikingly obvious. If such a chart is placed under good uniform illumination, and an observer is asked to tell you on which side of the card the gray background appears lighter, it is likely that he will report that the background is lighter on the side that has been cross-hatched with the white lines, and darker on the side that has been cross-hatched with the black lines. He will do this even though he has no difficulty at all in resolving the individual lines on the two sides of the figure. This can be confirmed, if necessary, simply by asking him to count them. Throughout this chapter we have noted repeatedly that a clearly delimited test stimulus of given luminance looks darker when placed next to a contrast inducing area of higher luminance. In the present example, however, although each element of the gray background has next to it a white area of higher luminance, it looks lighter rather than darker as the earlier discussions would have led us to expect. This particular phenomenon is called the Bezold spreading effect, and it derives its name from demonstrations reported in 1874 by a German scientist, W. von Bezold, who used colored areas overlaid with white arabesques and compared them with areas of the same color overlaid with black arabesques of the same design. The phenomenon, incidentally, is equally effective when the tracery is drawn or printed in different hues. The line color of the figure tends to pull the color of the background toward it, rather than accentuating the color difference, as occurs in the ordinary opponent contrast effects. The name "spreading effect" is a good descriptive phrase, and excellent illustrations of it may be seen in Evans' book, *An Introduction to Color.*

Helson and Rohles Experiment

Helson and Rohles have reported an experiment in which they used gray cards with patterns of vertical lines rather than cross-hatching. On one side of the card the lines were white and on the other black. The width of the lines was always 1 mm, but the distance between successive vertical lines was varied from 3 mm to 55 mm in different experimental series. Seen from a distance of 3 meters, the minimal separation of 3 mm subtends a visual angle of 3' 25" of arc and the maximal separation subtends a visual angle of 1° 3'. To estimate the magnitude of the effect they used a method of category scaling rather than a matching procedure. The observer judged the appearance of the gray background on the left with respect to the gray on the right and reported his judgments verbally. To do this he used 11 descriptive categories that varied from "very very much lighter," through "a little lighter," to "equal," or "a little darker" through "darker" and so on, up to "very, very much darker."

The spreading effect was greatest when the lines were separated by the smallest distance, and it decreased continuously with increase in line separation up to the largest separation between lines that was used. But even for the maximal separation of 1°3', the gray background lined with white still looked slightly lighter than the gray on which the lines were black.

Where the lines are closely spaced, the spreading effect might be attributable, at least to some extent, to the blurring of the retinal image that we have already discussed. In particular, stray light could be an important factor here. Ordinarily, when only a single boundary line is in question, the contrast mechanism can more than compensate for stray light spread over the parts of the image of different luminance. But in this kind of situation where the alternations between lighter and darker image areas occur repetitively at very close spatial intervals the contrast action could very well be overpowered by the spreading of stray light. Still, for stray light spread to account for the assimilation effect when each line is separated from its neighbors by a linear distance that is 55 times its own width seems unlikely.

Helson states that the assimilation phenomenon can be understood in terms of the kind of averaging that occurs where the luminance change from one stimulus element to the next is very small and uniform. We noted such averaging within the areas bounded by the contrast contours in the Mach ring demonstrations. Helson applies this principle to the spreading effect by assuming that area and luminance act in comparable ways and points to the fact that the assimilation phenomenon is most marked when the separation between adjacent lines is small. This cannot be quite the whole story, however, for we have also noted that visual resolution of small spatial gaps, or differences in luminance, is aided by the brightness *contrast* mechanism. Clearly, there is a continuum of effects that depend on the precise balance between processes of complementation and opposition, and this balance depends very critically on the spatial stimulus parameters.

SPATIAL AND TEMPORAL VARIABLES ACT
IN SIMILAR MANNER

On the whole, it seems obvious that the visual system handles spatial variations in stimulation in ways that seem directly comparable to the ways in which it handles variations in temporal stimulation. Here too, we have evidence that light stimulation of a given part of the retina is associated with an action process and that it also brings about a reaction in adjacent parts of the visual field. The action process is associated with the brightening effects, and the reaction process with darkening effects. With spatial differences in stimulation, the interplay between these two processes across small spatial extents may be such that the action—the positive brightening effect—of each stimulus is greater throughout a limited spatial extent, and then as the different stimuli are further separated, the reaction process—the opposite darkening effect—from the stronger stimulus then takes over. Thus the net effect on apparent brightness of spatial stimulus increments is a *brightening* for very small spatial extents, through *averaging* for slightly larger ones into *darkening* contrast.

BIBLIOGRAPHY

DIAMOND, A. L. Foveal simultaneous brightness contrast as a function of inducing- and test-field luminance. *J. exper. Psychol.*, 1953, 45, 304–314.

DIAMOND, A. L. Foveal simultaneous contrast as a function of inducing-field area. *J. exper. Psychol.*, 1955, 50, 144–152.

EVANS, R. M. *An Introduction to Color.* New York: Wiley, 1948.

GELB, A. Die Farbenkonstanz der Sehdinge. *Hand-d normal. u. path. Physiologie*, 1929, 12, 594–678.

HELSON, H., & ROHLES, F. A quantitative study of reversal of classical lightness-contrast. *Am J. Psychol.*, 1959, 72, 530–538.

HERING, E. *Outlines of a Theory of the Light Sense.* (English Translation, L. M. Hurvich and D. Jameson) Cambridge, Mass.: Harvard, 1964.

HESS, C., & PRETORI, H. Messende Untersuchungen über die Gesetzmässigkeit des simultanen Helligkeits-Contrastes. *Arch. f. Ophthal*, 1894, 40, 1–24.

HOCHBERG, J., & BECK, J. Apparent spatial arrangement and perceived brightness. *J. exper. Psychol.*, 1954, 47, 263–266.

LEIBOWITZ, H., MOTE, F. A., & THURLOW, W. R. Simultaneous contrast as a function of separation between test and inducing fields. *J. exper. Psychol.*, 1953, 46, 453–456.

MACH, E. *The Analysis of Sensations.* Chicago: Open Ct., 1914.

RATLIFF, F. *Mach Bands: Quantitative Studies on Neural Networks in the Retina.* San Francisco: Holden-Day, 1965.

WOODWORTH, R. S., & SCHLOSBERG, H. *Experimental Psychology.* (2nd Ed.) New York: Holt, 1954.

VI

Brightness Constancy

Throughout the preceding chapters of this book we have been describing the way in which perceived brightness depends upon stimulus luminance, stimulus size, viewing time, state of sensitivity of the visual system, rate of change of the spatial luminance gradient, a whole complex of variables, all of which alter the brightness that is perceived. Dark areas may appear in uniformly illuminated fields because of afterimages, lines or sharp edges may show up where they do not really "exist," and small brightness differences between objects may get larger or they may disappear as we change the state of adaptation or the illumination.

Everything we have said about our perceptions of brightness and darkness and the way these perceptual qualities relate to both stimulus and organismic variables could lead a careful reader to draw only one conclusion: chaos and confusion ought to prevail as far as our recognition of light and dark objects is concerned! As luminance increases objects get brighter. But does last night's raven-haired beauty become a platinum blonde in the full light of day? In spite of everything, all is not chaos and confusion, as we well know. Nor are the facts we have been summarizing and reviewing all false.

BRIGHTNESS CONSTANCY EXAMPLE

If you are reading this book indoors under moderate to good illumination, the white background of the page you are looking at probably has a luminance of approximately 15 mL. If the printer's ink is highly absorbent, it may reflect as little as 1 to 2 percent of the incident illumination, and the luminance of the letters that you are looking at (for 2 percent reflectance) may be as low as, say, 0.3 mL. With the same book outdoors on a moderately clear day, the luminance of the paper could easily be as high as 1500 mL (see Table 1), and in this case the luminance of the letters would be 30 mL, since the printer's ink would have the same reflectance value outdoors that it has in the indoor illumination situation. This means that the letters in outdoor light have twice the luminance (30 mL) that the paper of the page did in indoor light (15 mL). Do the letters now appear whiter than the paper was when the page was being read indoors? Obviously not. An observer who reported that the page looked white and the letters black under indoor illumination would almost certainly report again that the page looks white and the letters black when viewed outdoors. This common experience of visual perception that any one of us can verify is an example of what is known as brightness constancy.

So, despite all the complex ways in which we have said that perceived brightness can be shown to vary, we are now saying that we can all testify to an experience of brightness constancy. This state of affairs may seem paradoxical at first glance, but in fact it is not. In this chapter we shall try to examine some of the facts and experiments on the problem of brightness constancy in somewhat more detail, and we shall also try to show how these phenomena relate to the various factors that govern the changes in perceived brightness that we have been discussing in the earlier chapters.

Approximate Brightness Constancy

But we should keep in mind from the outset that there are limits to the "brightness constancy" phenomenon. Although the paper looks white and the letters black over a very wide range of their respective luminances, it is also true that we can tell a brighter sky from a less bright one at different times of day and at different times of the year, and most of us have no difficulty whatsoever in deciding when we want to add the light of a desk lamp to the general illumination in the room or when we would prefer to put on sunglasses to read outdoors. If there were really no change at all in the apparent brightness and apparent darkness of the page and the letters in the latter two instances, it would be difficult to account for our deciding that we ought to increase or decrease the level of illumination. Consequently, the visual problem with which we are to be concerned in this chapter is not truly brightness constancy, but is much more accurately described as "*approximate* brightness constancy."

Laboratory Experiment

Suppose that we bring our illustrative example into the laboratory where we can use a divided chamber apparatus of the sort that we have described in earlier chapters. On the left side of the dual chamber we place a paper of the same stock from which this book is made, and we illuminate this side of the chamber with a light source that duplicates the level of the indoor reading situation. The right-hand side of the chamber is illuminated with a photoflood light source that duplicates the level of the outdoor illumination. We may now seek, from a suitable sample of papers of different reflectances, that one which, under the strong illumination, appears identical in brightness to the test paper on the left under the weaker illumination.

The test paper has, say, a reflectance of 80 percent. Reflectance is a property of the paper and simply indicates what fractional part of the light that is incident upon it it will reflect. An alternative term for the reflectance of a surface is albedo, abbreviated, A. We shall use this term here since it occurs very frequently in the published literature concerned with the brightness constancy problem. Here the value of $A = 0.80$. The luminance, the light reflected from the surface towards the observer (see Chapter I), is a product of the incident illumination, illuminance, times the reflectance, and we may suppose that the test surface is illuminated at a level such that its luminance, L, is 15 mL. If we now were to use a photoelectric photometer, rather than a human eye, to determine the appropriate sample reflectance required in the strongly illuminated chamber for a match to the less strongly illuminated paper stock which is our test object, then the match will necessarily be a luminance match. The comparison sample reflectance R that gives a photometric reading on the right-hand side of the chamber that matches that of the test paper on the left is such that the product of R times its illumination level yields the same luminance value as the test luminance. The particular value of R required for a *stimulus luminance match*, either at the surface of the photocell or at the eye, we may call S. The value of S can always be computed when the test reflectance or albedo, A, the test illuminance I_t, and the illuminance, I_c, of the variable comparison surface are known.

$$A \times I_t = S \times I_c, \tag{1}$$

or

$$S = \frac{A \times I_t}{I_c} . \tag{2}$$

And, as we have just said, if the match is a photometric one made by a physical light-sensing device, then, R, the variable reflectance that is selected, is identical to the computed value of S. Moreover, if the human observer makes the matches by alternately viewing each of the two surfaces through a dark tube or aperture that screens all other light surfaces from view, he too will select as a match to the test object a surface of reflectance R that is also identical to the value of S. The greater the difference in illumination levels, of course, the greater the difference between $R(=S)$ and the reflectance of the test object, A.

Measures of Constancy

But we got into this problem by agreeing that the page we are reading, and whose reflectance is unchanged, appears fairly constant under very different levels of illumination, indoors and out. Here, R, the reflectance of the page under strong outdoor illumination, is identical to the reflectance of the same page in the relatively weak indoor light: $R = A, R \neq S$. If we actually produce a match in apparent brightness in the divided chamber setup in the laboratory, and if we do find that the sample reflectance, R, that is selected is identical to that of the test surface, A, then we can say that our observer shows complete brightness constancy. Typically, this result, namely, $R = A$, is not found, nor, except for the aperture situation, does $R = S$ in the brightness match experiments; instead, the observer is likely to select a value of R that lies between A and S. It is for this reason that various investigators have suggested specific formulas to represent the results of experiments of this sort in terms of *degree of constancy*. Thus, in the literature on brightness perception (as well as on other "constancies" such as size and shape), we find frequent reference to the Brunswik ratio and to the Thouless ratio. Both are ratio formulas derived to express the degree of constancy as measured by the reflectance values selected to obtain brightness matches across different illuminations.

Brunswik Ratio

The first of these two ratios is a formula proposed in 1929 by E. Brunswik, a well-known psychologist and student of perception who started his career in Germany and later moved to the University of California. The Brunswik ratio is expressed as follows:

$$\text{Constancy Ratio} = (R - S)/(A - S) \ . \tag{3}$$

We can see that in this formula, the difference between the comparison reflectance R that the observer selects for a brightness match to the test object and the computed reflectance S that is required for a stimulus luminance match is taken relative to the difference between the test object reflectance A and the same value of S again. Obviously, if the value of R chosen for a brightness match in the experimental situation we have described is identical to the value of S that is computed or determined photometrically, then there is zero brightness constancy: the observer is simply matching luminances, and in the formula $R - S = 0$. If, on the other hand, the observer selects a comparison sample whose reflectance is exactly that of the test sample when he makes his brightness match, then $R = A$, the Brunswik ratio is equal to unity, and this result is perfect brightness constancy: $R - S = A - S$ and $(R - S)/(A - S) = 1.0$.

Thouless Ratio

In studies of perceptual constancies reported in 1931, R. H. Thouless, a British psychologist, proposed a modified constancy ratio. Although the Brunswik ratio expresses accurately measures that indicate the two extremes, either of zero constancy or complete constancy, it was Thouless' view that the steps in between, for different degrees of approximate constancy, were not accurately represented by the numbers derived by Brunswik's formula. Thouless thought that a different formula was required in order to convert the differences between the numbers obtained into units that correspond more closely to equal *perceptual* steps. He proposed that the values that enter into the determination of the constancy ratio be transformed from arithmetic reflectance values to logarithms of these values. The formula for the Thouless ratio is thus:

$$\text{Constancy Ratio} = (\log R - \log S)/(\log A - \log S), \qquad (4)$$

where R, S, and A have the same meanings as in the Brunswik formula. We remember from the discussion of psychophysical scales that relate the perceived brightness of a stimulus field seen in isolation to the photometric luminance of that field (Chapter I) that Fechner's logarithmic relation was stated to be the classical and most frequently cited, although by no means universally accepted, psychophysical law. In view of this relation, a transformation from simple arithmetic values to their logarithms seems a not unreasonable step for Thouless to have proposed.

Proposed Modification

Woodworth and Schlosberg have suggested a different transformation of the values in the Brunswik ratio which explicitly derives from the results of brightness scaling experiments. They propose that the reflectance values expressed in the terms S, A, and R, be converted to "whiteness values" read from a scale determined experimentally by Newhall, Nickerson, and Judd in 1943.

Shortcomings of These Measures

The ratios of differences contained in all these formulas to express the degree of constancy obtained in a particular experiment can, however, lead to a certain amount of confusion. One sometimes reads, for example, that the degree of constancy that is found when observers are matching object colors under different levels of illumination is greater when the illumination differences increase. Does this mean that the reflectance of a variable comparison field must be changed less and less, relative to the standard test field, as the illumination on the comparison field is increased more and more, relative to that on the standard test surface? Typically, this kind of result is not found. What then is the basis for the report of increasing constancy? Let us consider a specific example. Suppose that we have a test object with a surface that reflects 50 percent of the incident light. Suppose further that this object is illuminated by 10 foot-candles of incident light. On the other side of our apparatus we have an illumination level of 20 foot-candles incident on a variable comparison surface whose average reflectance we can adjust until this surface appears to have the same brightness as our test object. Suppose that our observer does not show perfect constancy (that is, $R \neq 50$ percent), but finds that he must reduce the reflectance of the comparison field that is illuminated by the stronger light source to 45 percent in order to match the test surface of 50 percent reflectance seen under the lower level of illumination. We may now compute the Brunswik ratio for degree of constancy for this experimental result. The constancy ratio, $(R - S)/(A - S)$, would contain the following values.

A, the reflectance of the test object, equals 50 percent.

R, the reflectance of the comparison field as set by the observer, equals 45 percent.

The value of S, the reflectance that would be required under the doubled illumination level if the observer were making a stimulus luminance match, equals one half that of the test reflectance, equals 25 percent.

Thus,

$$\frac{R - S}{A - S} = \frac{45 - 25}{50 - 25} = \frac{20}{25} = 0.80$$

and the degree of constancy is 80 percent.

Let us now repeat the experiment, using the same test object of 50 percent reflectance at the same 10 foot-candle level of illumination, but this time we increase the illumination on the comparison field still more to a level of 100 foot-candles, which is 10 times the illuminance of the test object. Suppose that the observer again finds that he must reduce the average reflectance of the comparison field in order to obtain a brightness match to the test color, but the reflectance value that he now finds suitable is 43 percent. The value of S in this case is equal to 5, that is, one tenth the reflectance of the test object, to compensate for the tenfold increase in illumination on the comparison side. The value of the Brunswik ratio for this datum becomes

$$\frac{43 - 5}{50 - 5} = \frac{38}{45} = 0.84.$$

The degree of constancy has increased from 80 percent to 84 percent when the difference in illumination between the test and comparison fields was increased from a ratio of 2 to 1 to a ratio of 10 to 1.

If the same experimental data are expressed in terms of the Thouless ratio rather than the Brunswik formula, then we convert the values of A, R, and S to their logarithms. The logarithmic transformation gives us, for the situation where the illumination was doubled on the comparison side:

$$\frac{\log R - \log S}{\log A - \log S} = \frac{1.65 - 1.40}{1.70 - 1.40} = \frac{0.25}{0.30} = 0.83,$$

a value of 83 percent constancy. For the same example when the illumination was increased tenfold on the comparison side we have:

$$\frac{1.63 - 0.70}{1.70 - 0.70} = \frac{0.93}{1.00} = 0.93,$$

93 percent constancy. Again, the degree of constancy as expressed by the Thouless ratio increases when the illumination difference between the test and comparison objects is increased, in spite of the fact that the reflectance of the comparison field that is used for a match departs more from the reflectance of the test object for the larger difference in illumination than it does for the smaller one, which, of course, on the face of it implies a decrease in constancy.

It is possible, moreover, for these constancy ratios to have values greater than 1.0. We need only assume, in our example, that the observer matches to a test surface of $A = 0.50$ seen under 10 foot-candles of illumination, a comparison sample of $R = 0.55$ seen under 20 foot-candles. Both the Brunswik and Thouless ratios would now exceed 1.0, and constancy would be greater than perfect brightness constancy! Although such a result is unlikely for the particular experimental conditions we have postulated in this example, it is known to occur, and, because of the "degree of constancy" expressions, it has been called "overconstancy." We shall see in the later discussions the kinds of experimental conditions that are likely to yield such a result, and we shall there discuss it in a context that will make its perceptual significance more meaningful.

Luminance Ratio Measure

These difficulties have been recognized by a number of investigators, and other formulas to describe the same data simply express the measures in terms of a ratio of the luminances of the two areas, the test and the comparison, that are matched. These luminance ratios indicate departures, in one direction or another, from the value 1.0 that would be obtained for a photometric, stimulus luminance match in which test and comparison luminances would be identical. They do not indicate to what extent the deviant measures approximate matches of the *reflectances* of the two surfaces respectively, which is what the Brunswik and Thouless ratios were designed to do. As with the reflectance formulas, we find that some investigators prefer to convert the stimulus luminance ratio measure to a logarithmic value, as Helson does, for example. And, again, others use the luminance ratio of the two objects that are matched in apparent brightness and convert the values from photometric luminance to the particular scale of apparent brightness as given by the data of Newhall, Nickerson, and Judd for the Munsell spacing of achromatic samples that vary from black through gray to white.

CONCEPTUAL SCHEMAS

It may be useful at this point to summarize in a general way some of the ideas that have influenced the many experiments on brightness constancy and their interpretation. In addition to the two major figures, Helmholtz and Hering, who have had the greatest influence on the thinking of subsequent investigators of visual perception, the work of D. Katz, another German psychologist who later worked in Denmark, has played an important role in investigations of the brightness constancy problem.

Katz's Views

Katz emphasized, among other things, the different modes of appearance that a light image on our retinas can elicit under different conditions. If we look at a uniformly painted wall in an illuminated room, we typically see the wall as a surface, and in Katz's terminology we are seeing it in the "surface mode." Now if we roll up a piece of black paper to form a tube, place it close to one eye, and look through it at a part of the same

wall, then we will note that the color that we see through the tube has a
filmy appearance: we are now seeing the wall as a "film color." (The
viewing distance has to be far enough so that we are unable to detect
the grain or texture of the surface.) This latter mode of appearance is
often described as the "aperture mode" because this is, perhaps, the
easiest way to demonstrate it. But we may see the expanse of sky under
some conditions simply as a filmy expanse without the use of such an
aperture, although under other conditions it may actually take on the appearance of a vaulted, very distant surface. One of Katz's major points
was that brightness constancy effects occur under conditions which favor
the surface mode of color appearance, and they are essentially lacking for
lights seen in the aperture mode.

The separation of modes of appearance into aperture and surface
modes has influenced the thinking of many investigators, and it is fairly
common to find this distinction extended so that the word "brightness"
is limited to perceptions in the aperture mode and the word "lightness"
or "whiteness" is substituted for surface mode or "object color" perceptions. Although these distinctions can be useful in some situations,
their use can also sometimes obscure common properties and lawful relations that exist. They may also have led some experimenters to overlook
other aspects of their stimulus situations that were of direct relevance to
their experimental results. We shall return to this point below when we
discuss some specific experimental situations.

Helmholtz's Thinking

A common explanation for brightness constancy derives from Helmholtz's conceptualizations and analyses of the problems of perception.
Empiricism was at the heart of his thinking, and perceptions of objects
presumably came about by the building up of sensations—the core elements—into the more elaborate perceptions by way of experience. We
have touched upon Helmholtz's use of "unconscious inference" in the
discussion of contrast phenomena, but these inferences and judgments
also play a role in all perception. Judgment, particularly judgments about
the level and quality of illumination as distinct from the objects, play an
important role in the analysis of constancy effects. His thinking, which
is still influential in treatments of the constancy problem, is revealed in
the following statements. "A grey sheet of paper exposed to sunlight may
look brighter than a white sheet in the shade; and yet the former looks
grey and the latter white, simply because we know very well that if the
white paper were in the sunlight, it would be much brighter than the
grey paper which happens to be there at the time." "Colours have their
greatest significance for us insofar as they are properties of bodies and
can be used as marks of identification of bodies. Hence in our observa-

tions with the sense of vision we always start out by forming a judgment about the colours of bodies, eliminating the differences of illumination by which a body is revealed to us." ". . . it was noticed that in this sense we make a plain distinction between a dimly illuminated white surface and a highly illuminated grey one. Therefore, we have a certain difficulty about realizing that brightly lighted grey is the same as dimly lighted white. By some device the intense light must be confined strictly to the grey field, so that we cannot infer from the sense impression that the grey is more highly illuminated than the rest of the field of vision. It is then only that we recognize its identity with white." ". . . we are accustomed and trained to form a judgment of colours of bodies by eliminating the different brightness of illumination by which we see them . . ."

Thus we find in Helmholtz the basis for the view that we perceive the brightness qualities of surfaces correctly by distinguishing between the reflectance properties of the surface and the incident illumination, and either discounting or correcting for the illumination level. Some sort of learning process is assumed to be basic to the development of these capacities.

Hering's "Memory Color"

Hering also recognized the importance of experience. The way that he put it was that "all objects that are already known to us from experience or that we regard as familiar by their color, we see through the spectacles of memory color, and on that account quite differently from the way we would otherwise see them." For Hering, however, the more interesting problem was not the way that cognitive, inferential processes determine our visual perceptions, but rather it was to analyze the intrinsic capacities of the visual mechanisms that are responsible for our relatively stable perceptions despite widely varying stimulus conditions and that make it possible for us to develop stable "memory colors."

Stimulus Invariants

Still another approach to the perceptual constancy problem is to look for an invariant in the total stimulus field, one that can be correlated with the invariance of the perceptions. This is the point of view emphasized by a number of Gestalt psychologists, including the leading figure, W. Köhler. It has been explored in considerable detail by J. J. Gibson, primarily in space and form perception, and has been emphasized particularly by H. Wallach as the basic explanatory factor underlying brightness constancy.

Wallach's Ratio Concept

Wallach, for example, says that when the overall level of illumination on an array of surfaces is changed, the luminance of a particular surface is indeed altered, but since all luminances are altered proportionately, the luminance ratio of any one surface relative to any other in the total array remains constant. Hence luminance ratios provide the stimulus invariants with which our perceptions are to be correlated. There is no reason, in this view, why the visual system must respond to level of luminance as the basic stimulus variable, for it could very well alternatively be so organized as to respond to luminance ratio as a higher order stimulus variable. If this is so, there is no reason to expect anything but perfect brightness constancy as the illumination varies, since, if the objects themselves and their reflectances remain constant, as they do, then the ratios of their luminances must also be the same whatever the level of total illumination. Consequently, if we start from this view, then the problem that we have to investigate is not the reason for brightness constancy, but rather the reasons why this constancy is not complete but only approximate.

EXPERIMENTS

Wallach

Wallach's typical experimental setup uses four projectors. Slides in one pair of projectors provide one disk-ring stimulus combination and in the second pair of projectors another disk-ring combination. The two disk-ring combinations are projected next to each other on screens seen against a dark background, and episcotisters (see Chapter II) are used in front of all projectors to control independently the luminances of the four stimulus elements.

We know that a disk of fixed luminance can be made to vary in apparent brightness as the luminance of the ring or annulus is modified (Chapter V). If the luminance of the test disk is set, say, at 100 mL and the ring around it at 200 mL, at this luminance ratio of 1 to 2, the test disk appears to be a gray. With the luminance of the comparison ring set at 50 mL, the luminance of the comparison disk is adjusted until it appears to be of the same brightness as the test disk. This value turns out to be something of the order of 25 mL rather than 100 mL which would mean a stimulus luminance match. To achieve brightness equivalence between the test and comparison disks, the luminances of each disk-annulus combination have approximately the same ratio, namely 1 to 2. Other values of test and ring luminances have been employed, and the experimental data are always found to be closer to a luminance ratio match than to a simple match of the test and comparison disk luminances. A ratio match is only approximated in most cases, however, and it there-fore becomes important to ask whether the deviations simply reflect ran-dom variability, or whether there is something systematic about the deviations from a constant ratio match that could give us further insight into the mechanisms involved.

Hess and Pretori

A much earlier series of experiments that explored still greater ranges of luminances and luminance ratios than Wallach's was the classical study by Hess and Pretori that we referred to in the preceding chapter. Their apparatus, which we described in the last chapter, employed different means for varying the center and surround luminances, and their stimulus fields were square rather than circular. In essence, however, their experi-ments were very similar to Wallach's.

A sample of the experimental data reported by Hess and Pretori is given in Table 3. This table shows the test field luminance (in arbitrary

Table 3

Sample data from Hess and Pretori

Test luminance	Test to surround luminance ratio	Comparison luminance (L) and comparison to surround luminance ratio (r)										
		L	r	L	r	L	r	L	r	L	r	L	r
1.5	0.0007			64	0.0384	100	0.0371	200	0.0658	300	0.0938	512	0.1438
10	0.02	37	0.05	64	0.08	100	0.10	200	0.15			512	0.22
28	0.28	37	0.25	64	0.27	100	0.35	200	0.29	300	0.28	512	0.30
37	0.75	37	0.75	64	0.64	100	0.43	200	0.39	300	0.31	512	0.34
200	10.0							200	10.0	300	1.2	512	0.75

units) and the luminance ratio of the test to its surround. It also gives the luminance (L) of the comparison field that appears to match the test field when the comparison to surround luminance ratio (r) has the experimentally determined value shown. It is clear, first of all, that each test luminance can be matched by a whole range of different comparison field luminances provided the comparison surround is appropriately adjusted in each case. But, as we noted in the preceding chapter, we cannot say, from these data, that the test and comparison fields appear the same when the two bear the same luminance ratios to their respective surrounds. If we consider only the third row of the table, in which the test luminance is 28 and the test-to-surround ratio is 0.28, this does seem to be approximately true. There is some fluctuation about the value 0.28 for the experimentally determined comparison-to-surround luminance ratios, but the deviations do not show any obvious regularity. In all the other rows in the table, however, the ratio entries do show systematic variations. When the test luminance is 1.5 and the ratio to its surround is very low (0.0007), the comparison to surround ratios for the brightness match are not at all constant, but increase progressively as the luminance of the comparison field is increased. There is a systematic effect in the same direction, although smaller, for matches to the test field of luminance 10, for a test-to-surround ratio of 0.02. If we now examine row 4, where the test luminance is 37 and the test-to-surround ratio is 0.75, we again see a systematic trend in the experimentally determined comparison-to-surround ratios, but the trend here is in the opposite direction: the ratios decrease systematically for increasing values of comparison field luminance. And the last row, for which the test luminance is 200 and the test-to-surround ratio is 10.0, the ratio variation is again a decrease and one that is much more marked.

The most interesting and insight-provoking aspect of these ratio variations is that in addition to being systematic, the changes occur in two opposite directions. The reader who is struck by the full implications of these opposite variations from the constant ratio result will probably anticipate the essence of the next experiment to be described.

In the laboratory experiments that we have been discussing, a single test stimulus is presented in a uniformly illuminated surround area, and we have just seen that each time the luminance of the test field and its relation to the surround luminance is changed, the nature of the result is altered. But the viewing situation that we want ultimately to understand is not that of a single uniform surface on a homogeneous background. It is, rather, the situation in which we have a variety of objects or surfaces of different reflectances and in which the overall level of illumination may vary from time to time throughout a considerable range. Before we state the implications of the simple test-to-surround data for the normal, everyday, viewing situation therefore, it seems wise to see how well they hold up in a laboratory situation that more closely approximates the everyday one.

Complex Stimulus Pattern

A very simple way to set up such a viewing situation in the laboratory is to project on a screen a single slide made by photographing an array composed of a number of surfaces of different reflectances. Neutral density filters placed in the projector light beam can be used to vary the overall illumination of the projected sample array that is imaged on the screen without altering the relative luminance ratios of any one sample to the next. A comparison stimulus of continuously variable luminance is provided and is viewed in a uniform surround that is fixed in luminance. This comparison field is so located and shielded that it is not in the observer's field of view when he looks at the test array on the screen, but can be seen readily by simply turning his head at a right angle to the test screen. We now ask the observer to vary the comparison luminance to match, in turn, the brightness of each of the test samples. He does this for each level of overall illumination of the test samples that has been set in by the experimenter. The results of such an experiment are shown in Fig. 8A.

Figure 8A shows the log test luminance on the abscissa and the log matching luminance on the ordinate. The different symbols—circles, triangles, crosses, squares, and inverted triangles—are used to identify the five different test areas in the array. As the overall level of illumination is increased, the luminances of all test areas are increased proportionately. The comparison field luminances which the subject used to match the different test areas in brightness do not, however, show a common pattern for the three levels of increasing illumination. Areas 1, 2, and 3 all require an increase in matching luminance as the illumination is increased. These areas clearly do not exhibit brightness constancy, but all show some increase in brightness with increase in illumination level. Area 4, however, is matched by approximately the same comparison luminance at all three illumination levels. For this one test surface in the array we have brightness constancy. For area 5, the luminance of the matching field must be decreased as the illumination level is raised. Obviously, the more light coming from this test sample, the darker it looks! An unexpected finding, or is it?

What should we have anticipated from the Hess and Pretori data? If we look back at Table 3, we see that there was one test luminance (28) and one ratio of test-to-surround (0.28) for which the matching comparison to surround ratios were effectively constant, one result that implied perfect brightness constancy. When the test luminance was higher and when it bore a higher ratio to its surround luminance, then the matching comparison field did not bear a constant luminance ratio to its

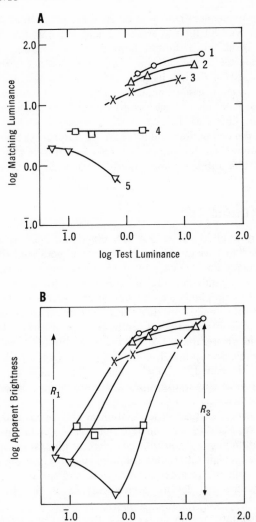

Figure 8. Measure of "approximate brightness constancy," and variations in psychophysical functions.

surround, but the surround luminance had to be increased relatively more than the comparison field to restore the same matching brightness. We can infer that the disproportionate increase in surround luminance was required because the comparison field appeared to increase in brightness when the two luminances increased in the same proportion. And this is precisely what we find for test areas 1, 2, and 3 in Fig. 8A. In Table 3, on the other hand, when the test luminance was low and the test-to-surround luminance ratio was also low, the luminance ratios for the matching comparison field to its surround showed a systematic increase with increase in comparison luminance. The surround luminance could not be increased as much as the comparison field to maintain the same comparison brightness as the test in these instances, and here we can infer that had the comparison and its surround luminances been increased in the same proportion, the comparison field would have grown increasingly darker. This inference directly anticipates the result of Fig. 8A for test area 5.

"Overconstancy" Clarified

We can now clarify from Fig. 8A the significance of a result of "overconstancy" that we mentioned in connection with the Brunswik and Thouless constancy ratios. Test area number 5 is becoming darker in appearance as the illumination level is increased. If we were to vary the reflectance of this sample to keep it constant in apparent brightness at the different levels of illumination, then the reflectance must be *increased* as the illumination is increased. This result, as we said earlier, will yield a constancy ratio greater than 1.0. To describe this result as "overconstancy," however, does not tell us the important fact, which is that, as illumination is increased, although some objects show no change in brightness and some appear to brighten, still others may appear to grow increasingly darker.

We can state a further generalization at this point, and it is that, in a given array, a surface of moderate reflectance (or luminance) relative to its surroundings may exhibit complete brightness constancy, surfaces of relatively high reflectance (or luminance) will show departures from constancy in the brightening direction, and surfaces of very low relative reflectance will deviate from constancy in the darkening direction.

What other information do we have about the brightness relations among these surfaces under different illuminations? Before we answer this question, we need to do still another experiment.

Conversion of Data to Brightness Units

In Fig. 8A, the units of measurement for the brightness changes are units of matching luminance. We know from Chapter I that units of luminance are not directly equivalent to units of perceived brightness, and we also know that many investigators of the approximate brightness constancy problem have recognized the need to transform their data to "perceptual" units based on some assumed or empirical psychophysical law or perceptual scale. A brief review of Chapter I reminds us, however, that one of the important variables that determines the form of a perceived brightness scale is the background against which the test lights are exposed. In the experiment of Fig. 8A, the matching luminances were established in a comparison field seen within a large homogeneously illuminated surround. The most direct way to measure the apparent brightnesses of our various matching luminance values is to have the same observers scale the comparison lights in the viewing situation of the original matching experiment. The particular procedure used in the study that we are describing to establish brightness scale units for the matching luminance values was that of brightness magnitude estimation, which was discussed in Chapter I.

When the data of Fig. 8A are converted to units of apparent brightness based on the experimentally determined brightness magnitude scale, the plots shown in Fig. 8B are obtained. The same symbols are maintained for the different test samples as in Fig. 8A, log test luminance is again plotted as abscissa, and log apparent brightness is now plotted as ordinate. An interesting feature of this figure relates to the question of brightness differences from one surface to the next and the way that these differences depend on level of illumination. The range of brightnesses associated with the total sample array at the lowest level of illumination used here is indicated by the vertical bar labelled R_1; the brightness range for the highest illumination is shown by R_3. The total range is expanded, perceptually, as the illumination is raised, even though the reflectance properties of the test objects are unchanged. This expanded range is, of course, a direct consequence of the departures from brightness constancy in both the brightening and darkening directions. And the increase in apparent contrast between light and dark objects is a characteristic that we recognize as typical of a change from relatively dim to strong illumination.

Multiplicity of Psychophysical Relations

To return to our example of the white paper and black letters, if the white paper has a reflectance that approximates test area 1, and the black letters, area 5, then it is obvious that the paper will continue to look white and the letters black as the illumination is increased. But it is now also obvious why, if we are reading under the low level of illumination, we might prefer to turn on a desk lamp, if the result we have come to associate with the higher illumination is the increase in perceived contrast from R_1 to R_3. The reader may remember that we mentioned precisely this effect of illumination increase in discussing brightness discrimination (Chapter III) and also at the end of Chapter I. We pointed out there that when we are exploring the way in which perceived brightness increases with stimulus luminance, and when we are concerned with methods of scaling, the influence of background level, and the form of the psychophysical law, we should not forget that in our everyday experience we have evidence that the perceived brightness function need not even bear a single *directional* relation to stimulus luminance. Fig. 8B makes it clear that the very idea of *a* psychophysical law that relates perceived brightness to stimulus luminance must be interpreted to have only very specialized and restricted meaning. The curves drawn in this figure describe not one but eight different psychophysical relations, and they differ not only in form but also in sign.

A family of curves such as these, then, is our more general picture of the relation between brightness and luminance and it is also our more general description of "approximate brightness constancy."

FACTORS CONTRIBUTING TO APPROXIMATE BRIGHTNESS CONSTANCY

Throughout the preceding chapters we have discussed a number of aspects of the visual mechanism that play various roles in determining our brightness perceptions. Let us now look at some of these to see in what ways, if any, they may contribute to the rather complex phenomenon of approximate brightness constancy as we now understand it.

Pupil Size

We have seen that when the level of illumination is very high, the pupil of the eye constricts to its narrowest diameter, and when the level of illumination is very low, the pupillary aperture widens. The narrowest diameter of the natural pupil under very bright illumination is approximately 2 mm. As the illumination is reduced to very low levels, the pupil can widen to approximately 6 mm or, in some cases, to as much as 8 mm. Since the amount of light passing through an aperture is proportional to the area of the aperture, then a threefold variation in pupillary diameter would produce a ninefold variation in *retinal* illuminance, if the external illumination were constant. Hence, we see that the pupillary response of widening and constriction actually serves to reduce the range of retinal illuminances to a considerably smaller total range than the range of illumination levels outside the eye. The pupillary response partially compensates, therefore, for the variation in level of illumination in the environment. This compensatory mechanism has a proportional effect on all stimulus levels, and maintains the stimulus luminance ratios unchanged, while restricting the overall increase.

Adaptation and Sensitivity Level

Secondly, we have seen that even if an artificial pupil is used that is fixed in diameter and smaller than the minimal value of the natural pupil, the sensitivity of the visual system, as measured by the smallest amount of light that can be detected, is adjusted to different levels depending on the level of general illumination to which the eye is exposed. This general adaptation process adjusts the visual light sensitivity to an average level of illumination in such a way that the system is more sensitive when the general illumination is very weak, and less sensitive when the eye is exposed to a very high level of external illumination. The general adaptation process, moreover, not only affects visibility, which is concerned with the minimal light level that we can detect, it also influences the apparent brightnesses of all light levels, high and low, to which the eye is exposed. The extent of this influence of adaptation we discussed earlier in connection with the dependence of brightness on time, where we cited the results of Craik's experiments. To repeat the extreme example, a steadily fixated test area of as much as 1000 mL in one eye, when the eye had adapted to it, appeared only as bright as a stimulus of about 3 mL that was presented briefly to the other eye that remained dark-adapted, and thus maximally light sensitive. Craik's experimental situation is, of course, not typical of the way that we normally view the illuminated world for useful vision, but it does illustrate the extent to which the general adaptation process can compensate for the variations in incident level of illumination to which the eyes are exposed. The sensitivity changes associated with the general adaptation process are usually thought to resemble pupillary changes in the sense that the effects are proportional for all stimulus luminances. If this usual assumption is correct, then the responses to all luminance levels would be proportionally reduced as sensitivity is decreased; such a mechanism would therefore account for a generalized "damping" of apparent brightness changes with increase in illumination, but it would not, without additional assumptions, account for the different kinds and directions of change that we observe.

Successive or Local Adaptation

The complex brightness effects that we wish to explain occur not when our eyes are exposed to large areas of uniform luminance, but rather in the everyday viewing situation that includes an array of objects of different luminances that we fixate successively with the same part of the retina as we look from one part of the field of view to another. Consequently, the third factor that we may examine is that of local, or what has been called by Hering, successive adaptation, that is brought about by eye movements. Since the same part of the retina is successively illuminated with parts of the image that are respectively lighter and darker than the average of the retinal illuminance of the image of the visual field as a whole, there are local fluctuations in sensitivity about the general average that is set by the general overall level of illumination. This fluctuating, successive, local adaptation effect prevents the continuation of the general adaptation process to the extent where it would wash out all perceived brightness differences among the different parts of the visual field and continue to a state of overall equilibrium for which no useful vision is possible. The latter possibility, we remember, is realized only when special devices are used to eliminate the effectiveness of eye movements in varying the stimulation on specific parts of the retina from one moment to the next. If it were not for the fluctuating, successive local adaptation that accompanies eye movements, then we would indeed have a sort of brightness constancy, but, unless we blinked or shut our eyes periodically, we would "see" the world "blindly" as a uniform, undifferentiated mid-gray.

Successive Induction

There is another factor that is involved when the level of light stimulation on a given part of the retina is varied from one moment to the next. This is the aftereffect, back-reaction process that is most easily seen when afterimages occur. Although a number of visual scientists group these afterimage effects together with local, successive variations in sensitivity under the general category of adaptation, we list them separately here. Unquestionably, an ongoing reaction process in the visual system will have an influence on the sensitivity of that system to the action of a light stimulus. We can, on the other hand, envisage particular physiological changes that would alter the sensitivity of the system without implying such ongoing reaction processes. An example is the depletion of photosensitive absorbing material in the retina, which would obviously reduce light sensitivity, but need not at all imply ongoing events of the sort that we refer to here. For these successive aftereffects, or reaction events, we may use the term employed by Hering, namely, successive induction. Qualitatively, although the quantitative laws may be quite different, the successive induction process would lead to effects comparable to the effects of successive, local adaptation. If, for example, a given part of the retina is illuminated successively, first by a relatively intense part of the image and secondly by a relatively less intense part, then the aftereffect of the stimulation by the high illumination will be a reaction process that is darkening, and this ongoing darkness process will occur at the same time that the less intensely illuminated part of the image falls on that same area of the retina. Hence, like the local adaptation process, successive induction serves to accentuate local differences in brightness in the visual field.

Simultaneous Opponent Induction

Finally, we have the simultaneous opponent induction events that are brought about by spatial interactions among activities in different parts of the retina. This is the accentuation-of-difference process known as simultaneous contrast, and as we have seen, the effects can be observed even when the role of eye movements has been eliminated by using extremely short flash exposures of the stimulus field.

Interaction effects are, of course, sensitive to stimulus changes anywhere in the visual field, and it is for this reason that when we use a dark viewing tube to look at a particular stimulus area we are usually drastically changing the induced activity processes by eliminating all the light stimulus elements in the surround. It hardly seems adequate or even necessarily helpful to our understanding to describe this kind of change simply as a change from the object or surface mode to the film or aperture mode of appearance.

The simultaneous induction process due to spatial interaction again has qualitative, if not quantitative, similarities to the effects of both local successive adaptation and successive induction. It serves to accentuate brightness differences among differently illuminated elements of the visual field.

But the induction process is conceived as having an effect that differs in an important respect from the effects of pupil size and of simple sensitivity changes. That is, it produces an incremental (additive or subtractive) rather than a proportional (multiplicative) change. To recognize the significance of this difference, suppose we have two individual light stimuli which, when viewed separately each against a dark background, evoke brightness responses of magnitudes 10 and 100 respectively. Now if a large illuminated background is introduced, and this brings about a reduction in light sensitivity to one half its original value, then, by the usual assumption, the brightness responses to the two separate test stimuli will also be reduced to one half, namely, to 5 and 50, respectively. The perceived brightnesses still stand in the same ratio of 1 to 10.

The opponent induction caused by the illuminated surround has the effect of *subtracting* the same brightness amount from the response to both stimuli. If we let this amount equal, say, 5, then the original responses would be reduced to 5 and 95, respectively. The perceived brightness ratio is thereby altered, here, to 1 to 19 rather than 1 to 10. It is consequently the incremental character of the induction process that accounts for the kinds of deviations from brightness constancy that we observe, departures from constancy in both the brightening and darkening directions, changes in relative brightness among different areas, and so on.

Detailed mathematical expressions for the various processes described here have been worked out, and computed theoretical functions have been compared with many of the experimental data described or presented in the various chapters of this book. The interested reader can find these precise theoretical treatments in the references. Our primary objective here is to convey the essential principles involved in the operation of the visual mechanism as one governed by adaptive properties that enable it to encompass the very wide ranges of stimulus energies to which it is exposed on different occasions, and one characterized by dual response processes that, when stimulated by light, give rise to both white and black perceptual qualities, to both brightening and darkening effects.

PHOTOCHEMISTRY AND NEUROPHYSIOLOGY

Very little has been said about the details of the physiological events underlying the operation of this visual mechanism. Actually much is known about some, though not all, aspects of retinal photochemistry and the bleaching and regeneration that occurs when the eye is exposed to light and allowed to recover in darkness. Much work has also been done to record the neuroelectrical events associated with the eye as a whole, the optic nerve, and individual neural elements in the retina, optic nerve, lateral geniculate body, and even the visual cortex. We know something of the way the individual elements are organized into receptive fields and can relate this organization both to summation effects of light stimulation and to opponent interactions. A direct analogy to the Mach ring phenomenon can even be demonstrated in an electrophysiological experiment on neural interaction in a lower organism. The details of the physiological picture, although still only fragmentary, make a fascinating story in themselves, but that story is beyond the scope of this book.

BIBLIOGRAPHY

BRUNSWIK, E. Zur Entwicklung der Albedowahrnehmung. *Zeit. f. Psychol.*, 1929, **109**, 40–115.
DARTNALL, H. J. A. *Visual Pigments*. London: Methuen, 1957.

GELB, A., Die Farbenkonstanz der Sehdinge. *Handbuch der normalen und pathologischen Physiologie*, 1929, **12**, 594–678.

GIBSON, J. J. Perception as a function of stimulation. In *Psychology: A Study of a Science* (S. Koch, Ed.). New York: McGraw-Hill, 1959.

GRANIT, R. The visual pathway. In *The Eye* (H. Davson, Ed.). Vol. II. New York: Academic Press, 1962.

HELMHOLTZ, H. v. *Physiological Optics.* (3rd ed.) (English Translation, J. P. C. Southall) Vol. II. New York: Optical Society of America, 1924. Pp. 131, 286, 287.

HELSON, H. Some factors and implications of color constancy. *J. opt. Soc. Amer.,* 1943, **33**, 555–567.

HELSON, H. *Adaptation-Level Theory.* New York: Harper, 1964.

HERING, E. *Outlines of a Theory of the Light Sense.* (English Translation, L. M. Hurvich and D. Jameson) Cambridge, Mass.: Harvard, 1964. Section 4.

HESS, C., & PRETORI, H. Messende Untersuchungen über die Gesetzmässigkeit des simultanen Helligkeitscontrastes. *Arch. Ophthal.,* 1894, **40**, 1–24.

HSIA, Y. Whiteness constancy as a function of difference in illumination. *Arch. Psychol.,* 1943, No. 284.

JAMESON, D., & HURVICH, L. M. Opponent-colors theory and physiological mechanisms. In *The Visual System: Neurophysiology and Psychophysics* (R. Jung and H. Kornhuber, Eds.). Berlin: Springer-Verlag, 1961. Pp. 152–161.

JAMESON, D., & HURVICH, L. M. Theory of brightness and color contrast in human vision. *Vision Research,* 1964, **4**, 135–154.

KATZ, D. *The World of Colour.* (English Translation, R. B. MacLeod and C. W. Fox) London: Kegan Paul, Trench, Trubner & Co., 1935.

KOFFKA, K. *Principles of Gestalt Psychology.* New York: Harcourt, 1935.

KÖHLER, W. *Gestalt Psychology: An Introduction to New Concepts in Modern Psychology.* New York: Liveright, 1947.

LEIBOWITZ, H. Relation between the Brunswik and Thouless ratios and functional relations in experimental investigations of perceived shape, size and brightness. *Percept. mot. Skills.,* 1956, **6**, 65–68.

MACLEOD, R. B. Brightness constancy: An experimental investigation of brightness constancy. *Arch. Psychol.,* 1932, No. 35.

NEWHALL, S. M., NICKERSON, D., & JUDD, D. B. Final report of the OSA Subcommittee on the spacing of the Munsell Colors. *J. opt. Soc. Amer.,* 1943, **33**, 385–418.

THOULESS, R. H. Phenomenal regression to the real object, I. *Brit. J. Psychol.,* 1931, **21**, 339–359.

WALLACH, H. Brightness constancy and the nature of achromatic colors. *J. exp. Psychol.,* 1948, **38**, 310–324.

WOODWORTH, R. S., & SCHLOSBERG, H. *Experimental Psychology.* (Rev. ed.) New York: Holt, 1954.

Index